NELSON

UNIV

BIOLOGY 12

STUDY GUIDE

SENIOR PROGRAM CONSULTANT

Maurice DiGiuseppe, Ph.D.
University of Ontario Institute of Technology (UOIT)
Formerly of Toronto Catholic District School Board

PROGRAM CONSULTANT

Douglas Fraser B.Sc., B.Ed.
District School Board Ontario North East

NELSON EDUCATION

NELSON EDUCATION

Nelson Biology 12 Study Guide

Senior Program Consultant
Maurice DiGiuseppe

Program Consultant
Douglas Fraser

Student Book Authors
Douglas Fraser
Barry LeDrew
Angela Vavitsas
Meredith White-McMahon

Editorial Director
Linda Allison

Associate Publisher, Science
David Spiegel

Managing Editor, Science
Jennifer Hounsell

Product Manager
Doug Morrow

Program Manager
Carmen Yu

Project Managers
Christine Robson-Doucette
First Folio Resource Group Inc.:
Eileen Jung

Project Team
First Folio Resource Group Inc:
Julie Kretchman
Michael Pidgeon

Design Director
Ken Phipps

Interior Design
Courtney Hellam

Cover Design
Jarrel Breckon
Eugene Lo
Ken Phipps

Cover Image
RNA polymerase transcription:
© Laguna Design/Science Photo
Library

Asset Coordinator
Suzanne Peden

Illustrators
Steve Corrigan
Deborah Crowle
Sharon and Joel Harris
Ann Sanderson
MPS Limited
Nesbitt Graphics, Inc.

Compositor
MPS Limited

Cover Research
Debbie Yea

Printer
Transcontinental Printing

Reviewers
The authors and publisher gratefully
acknowledge the contributions of
the following educators:
Brent Campbell
Meredith White-McMahon

Contents

Biochemistry

Chapter 1: The Biochemical Basis of Life

Matter makes up everything in the universe, including all living organisms. All matter is composed of elements. Elements, in turn, are made up of atoms, which react with one another in predictable ways based on their structure and their electronegativity. The reactions we observe between biological molecules all depend on the characteristics of the atoms that make up the molecules and how they interact.

One of the most important chemicals for life is water. Water makes up a large part of every living organism and its surface tension, ability to dissolve polar compounds, and reactivity with acids and bases are critical to maintaining life processes.

Carbohydrates, lipids, proteins, and nucleic acids are also important biological chemicals. Carbohydrates are used as an energy source, as building materials, and for cell communication. Lipids form cell membranes, serve as hormones, and are used to store energy in cells. Proteins carry out several structural and functional roles in the cell. Nucleic acids join into long chains to form strands of DNA, which store hereditary information, and of RNA, which transfer information to build new proteins.

Chapter 2: Cell Structure and Function

Every cell in every living organism has a specific role. Organelles within the cell carry out specific functions to help the cell perform its role. A membrane surrounds every cell and controls access to it. This protects the cell and ensures that it has raw materials available for all of the reactions it carries out, and that products and waste materials are carried away. A membrane also surrounds and controls access to many of a cell's organelles.

Membranes have a fluid mosaic structure that enables them to carry out their role. Small, non-polar molecules are able to diffuse through the membrane freely. Transport proteins located in the membrane help important polar substances to cross the membrane and in some cases move against the concentration gradient. The processes of endocytosis and exocytosis enable large nutrients and waste molecules to cross the membrane.

Our growing understanding of cell components and processes has led to the ongoing development of nanotechnology: extremely tiny tools that can be used for medical diagnosis and treatment. Research in this expanding field will likely change the ways many diseases are diagnosed and treated.

BIG IDEAS

- Technological applications that affect biological processes and cellular functions are used in the food, pharmaceutical, and medical industries.

- Biological molecules and their chemical properties affect cellular processes and biochemical reactions.

- Biochemical compounds play important structural and functional roles in cells of all living organisms.

The Fundamental Chemistry of Life

Textbook pp. 8–18

Vocabulary

isotope	anion	dehydration reaction
radioisotope	polar covalent bond	hydrolysis reaction
orbital	polarity	neutralization reaction
valence electron	intermolecular force	redox reaction
ionic bond	van der Waals forces	oxidation
cation	hydrogen bond	reduction

MAIN IDEA: Protons and neutrons are located in the nucleus of an atom, and electrons surround the nucleus. Isotopes are different forms of the same element, with different numbers of neutrons. A radioisotope is an unstable isotope that decays to release particles.

1. Complete **Table 1** by writing the atomic number and mass number of each element and sketching the nucleus. K/U C

Table 1 Atomic Structure

Element	Symbol	Atomic number	Mass number	Diagram of nucleus
carbon	$^{12}_{6}C$			
nitrogen	$^{14}_{7}N$			
sodium	$^{23}_{11}Na$			
chlorine	$^{35}_{17}Cl$			

2. Draw a flow chart to show the reactants and products when the radioactive isotope ^{14}C decays. K/U C

3. Use **Table 2** to summarize the positive applications and negative effects of radioisotopes. K/U C

Table 2 Radioisotope Pros and Cons

Pros	Cons

MAIN IDEA: Valence electrons are the electrons in the outermost energy shell of an atom.

4. Use the properties of valence electrons to explain each scientific result. K/U T/I

   (a) Sodium bonds readily with chlorine.

   (b) Oxygen readily combines with magnesium but also with carbon.

5. Lewis dot diagrams show the electrons in an atom's outer energy shell. For example, the Lewis dot diagram for carbon is $\cdot\overset{\cdot}{\underset{\cdot}{C}}\cdot$. Draw a Lewis dot diagram for each of the following elements. C

   (a) oxygen

   (c) boron

   (b) fluorine

   (d) neon

MAIN IDEA: There are four types of chemical bonds in biochemistry: ionic, covalent, hydrogen bonds, and weak van der Waals forces.

6. Each molecule in **Table 3** below includes an ionic bond. Name the anion and the cation that bond in each. K/U T/I

Table 3 Anions and Cations

Molecule	Anion	Cation
sodium chloride, NaCl		
potassium chloride, KCl		
magnesium oxide, MgO		
calcium chloride, $CaCl_2$		

7. Each molecule below includes a covalent bond. Draw a diagram of each bond. Use a dash to represent the shared electrons. K/U C

   (a) hydrogen, H_2

   (c) chlorine, Cl_2

   (b) ammonia, NH_3

   (d) carbon dioxide, CO_2

MAIN IDEA: Electronegativity is a measure of an atom's attraction for electrons. Differences in electronegativity results in bond polarity. Intermolecular forces are attractive forces between molecules.

8. Add δ^- and δ^+ symbols to each diagram to show the positively and negatively charged parts of the molecule. T/I C

(a) H_2O
(Hydrogen is more electronegative than oxygen.)

(c) methanol
(Carbon is approximately as electronegative as hydrogen, but less electronegative than oxygen.)

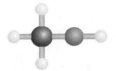

(b) CO_2
(Oxygen is more electronegative than carbon.)

d) O_2

9. When two atoms form a hydrogen bond the properties of the atoms change in the resultant molecule. Describe five changes that occur in the physical properties of the resultant molecule as a result of hydrogen bonding. K/U

10. Complete each sentence to explain how weak van der Waals forces to each of the following. K/U

(a) Large, non-polar octanes are liquid at room temperature because _____

_____

(b) Linear cellulose molecules can form long strands because _____

_____

MAIN IDEA: Dehydration is the removal of —OH and —H from two reactant molecules to form a larger molecule and water. Hydrolysis occurs when a bond in a large molecule is broken, and water is added to the resulting subunits.

11. Diagram _____ depicts a dehydration reaction and diagram _____ depicts a hydrolysis reaction. K/U

A

B

12. Why are dehydration reactions important in biology? T/I

MAIN IDEA: A neutralization reaction is a reaction between an acid and a base to produce a salt and water. Oxidation is the loss of electrons, and reduction is the gain of electrons. The oxidation of one molecule or atom is always linked to the reduction of another molecule or atom. This is called a redox reaction.

13. Nitric acid, HNO_3, is added to potassium hydroxide, KOH. Which chemical equation represents the chemical reaction? K/U T/I
    (a) $HNO_3 + KOH \rightarrow KNO_3 + H_2O$
    (b) $HNO_3 + H_2O \rightarrow KNO_3 + KOH$
    (c) $HNO_3 + KOH \rightarrow KHNO_3 + HO$
    (d) $HNO_3 + KNO_3 \rightarrow KOH + H_2O$

14. Label the oxidation reaction, the reduction reaction, the oxidizing agent, and the reducing agent. Circle the electrons, or the atoms, that are transferred. K/U

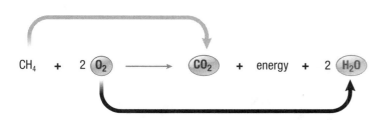

Water: Life's Solvent

Vocabulary

specific heat	hydrophilic	strong base
cohesion	hydrophobic	weak acid
surface tension	autoionization	weak base
adhesion	strong acid	neutralization reaction
buffer		

MAIN IDEA: Water forms a lattice structure through hydrogen bonding. The hydrogen bonding of water molecules to one another gives water a high surface tension.

1. Use **Table 1** to describe the characteristics of water's lattice structure that allow each phenomenon and explain why it is important for life. T/I C

Table 1 Water's Structure and Importance

Phenomenon	Characteristics of lattice	Importance to life
Ice is less dense than water.		
Water is liquid over a wide range of temperatures.		

2. What property of liquid water's lattice structure causes surface tension? K/U

MAIN IDEA: As polar molecules or charged ions dissolve in solution, they are completely surrounded by water molecules, which reduce the electrostatic interactions between them.

3. **Figure 1** shows table salt (sodium chloride) dissolving in water. Add labels to the dissolved ions and the surrounding water molecules to show electrostatic attractions creating a hydration shell and dissolving the ions. K/U

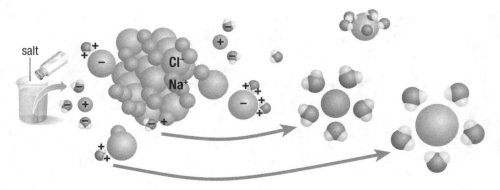

Figure 1

4. _____ molecules are not strongly attracted to water molecules, while _____ molecules are strongly attracted to water molecules. K/U

MAIN IDEA: The proper pH of cells inside living organisms and their environment is critical for the survival of the organisms.

5. The pH scale has a numerical range from 0 to 14 which depends on the concentration of hydronium and/or hydroxide ions in solution. Write the pH value for each item below. K/U T/I
   (a) very high concentration of OH^- ions _____
   (b) very high concentration of H_3O^+ ions _____
   (c) very acidic _____
   (d) very basic _____
   (e) blood _____
   (f) ten times as acidic as pH 4 _____
   (g) balance of OH^- and H_3O^+ ions _____

6. Describe three biological processes that depend on a specific pH. T/I

STUDY **TIP**

pH Scale
Make your own copy of the pH scale found on page 22 of your textbook. Use other products for examples of certain pHs.

MAIN IDEA: Strong acids and bases dissociate completely in water. Weak acids and bases dissociate only partially in water. Acids and bases react to form water and a salt in neutralization reactions.

7. Why are most acids and bases involved in biochemical reactions weak? A

8. Why is the following reaction called a neutralization reaction? Label the key parts of the reaction. K/U T/I

$$HCl\ (aq) + NaOH \rightarrow H_2O + NaCl\ (aq)$$

MAIN IDEA: A buffer is a weak acid or base that can compensate for changes in a solution to maintain the proper pH level.

9. The following reaction shows how carbonic acid keeps blood pH within a narrow range. C A

$$H_2CO_3 \leftrightarrow HCO_3^- + H^+$$

   (a) Label the following:
   • the direction the reaction proceeds in to buffer acidic blood
   • the direction the reaction proceeds in to buffer basic blood
   (b) Explain how you decided which direction the reaction would proceed in.

The Carbon Chemistry of Life

Vocabulary
functional group

MAIN IDEA: Carbon atoms form the backbone of biological molecules. They can link together to form chains, branched structures, and rings.

LEARNING TIP

C–H Bonds
Remember a carbon atom has six electrons and a hydrogen atom has one electron to share.

1. Draw the structural diagrams for the following hydrocarbons. Label each carbon atom and hydrogen atom. `C`

   (a) methane, CH_4

   (c) a simple hydrocarbon chain

   (b) a hydrocarbon ring

   (d) a hydrocarbon with a double bond

2. What characteristic of carbon atoms allows molecules that include them to assume so many shapes? `K/U`

3. Are molecules that contain only hydrogen-carbon bonds polar? Why or why not? `T/I`

MAIN IDEA: Functional groups have polar or ionic qualities that influence how they interact with water and other molecules.

4. Draw a structural diagram of each functional group and provide an example of a biological molecule that contains it. `K/U` `C`

   (a) alcohol

   (c) carboxyl

   (b) amino

   (d) phosphate

5. Describe the characteristics of each functional group that make it acidic or basic. K/U

   (a) —C—COOH _____

   (b) —C—NH$_2$ _____

   (c) —C—PO$_4{}^{2-}$ _____

MAIN IDEA: A dehydration reaction involves the removal of water from subunits as they combine to form a larger molecule. A hydrolysis reaction involves large molecules reacting with water to be broken down into smaller subunits.

6. Sketch a diagram to show how two sugar molecules combine to create a larger molecule through dehydration. Use a hexagon to represent the hydrocarbon ring in each sugar molecule. Show what is added to or taken away from the sugar molecules as they bond. C

7. Sketch a diagram to show how a large carbohydrate molecule undergoes hydrolysis to form smaller simple sugar molecules. Use a hexagon to represent the hydrocarbon ring in each sugar molecule. Show what is added to or taken away from the molecules as the bonds are broken. C

8. Which statement describes the function of a hydrolysis reaction and which statement describes the function of dehydration reaction? T/I

   (a) This reaction breaks starches and sugars down to release energy.

   _____

   (b) This reaction creates starch molecules to store energy.

   _____

Carbohydrates and Lipids

Vocabulary

carbohydrate	polysaccharide molecule	triglyceride
monosaccharide	polymerization	saturated fat
isomer	monomer	unsaturated fat
disaccharide	polymer	phospholipid
glycosidic bond	lipid	steroid
complex carbohydrate	fatty acid	wax

MAIN IDEA: Carbohydrates are simple and complex sugar molecules. They are the most abundant macromolecules found in living things on Earth. Monosaccharides are single sugar molecules that have a 1:2:1 ratio of C:H:O. Disaccharides consist of two single sugar subunits, which are linked through a dehydration synthesis reaction. Polysaccharides are long chains of sugar monomers.

1. List three ways that carbohydrates are used by cells. K/U

> ### LEARNING TIP
>
> **Chemical Ratios**
> Certain types of compounds have a specific ratio of component atoms. Remember them and you will be able to recognize a compound.

2. Fructose is a typical monosaccharide. Complete the diagram of fructose (**Figure 1**) and write its chemical formula. K/U C

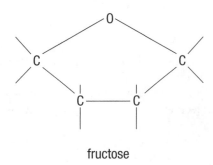

fructose

Figure 1

3. Explain the similarities and differences between α-glucose and β-glucose. T/I

4. Complete the following chemical reaction and explain what occurs in the reaction. K/U C

glucose + glucose → maltose +

5. Describe, and give an example of, a disaccharide with a $1 \rightarrow 4$ linkage. [K/U]

6. The formation of polysaccharide molecules is an example of _____.
   Monosaccharide molecules or _____ bond together through
   a _____ reaction to form polysaccharide molecules
   or _____. [K/U]

MAIN IDEA: Carbohydrates are polar molecules. They are soluble in water, unless they are very large. Lipids are generally non-polar molecules that do not readily dissolve in water.

7. Use **Table 1** to compare and contrast lipids with complex carbohydrates. [T/I] [C]

Table 1 Lipids and Complex Carbohydrates

Lipids	Complex carbohydrates

8. List four main biological functions of lipids. [K/U]

MAIN IDEA: Fatty acids and triglycerides are primarily energy storage molecules. Triglycerides consist of three fatty acid chains linked to glycerol.

9. (a) Why are saturated fatty acids more likely to be solid at room temperature than unsaturated fatty acids?

   (b) Why are mammals and birds more likely than other animals to store energy as saturated fats? [K/U] [T/I]

1.4 Carbohydrates and Lipids   **11**

10. Label the molecules that form the triglyceride in **Figure 2**. K/U T/I C

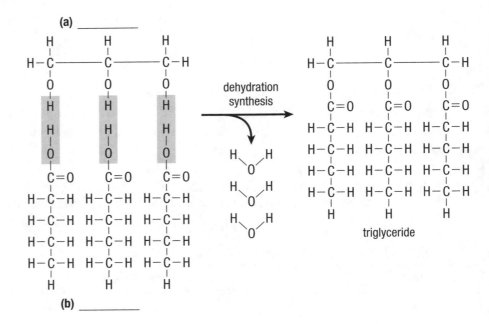

Figure 2

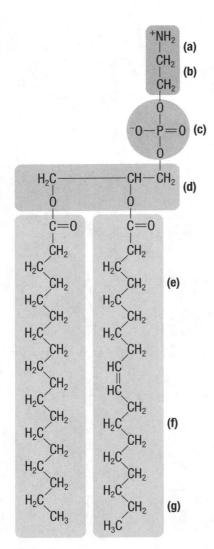

MAIN IDEA: Phospholipids are the main component of all plasma membranes. They are formed from a glycerol molecule, two fatty acids, and an ionic phosphate-containing group. Steroids are small lipids with a four-carbon ring structure. Waxes are long fatty acid chains linked to alcohol or ring structures. They function primarily as waterproofing compounds.

11. Identify the parts of the phospholipid in **Figure 3**. K/U

___ polar   ___ glycerol

___ non-polar   ___ hydrophilic head

___ fatty acid chain   ___ hydrophobic tail

___ phosphate group

12. Describe how the structure of cholesterol and phytosterols enable these steroids to perform their function. K/U

13. Describe two harmful effects of steroids in humans. K/U

14. Many different organisms use or produce wax for different functions. Name three organisms that use or produce wax and describe the function of the wax in these organisms. K/U

Figure 3

Proteins and Nucleic Acids

Vocabulary

protein	peptide	nucleotide
nucleic acid	polypeptide	phosphodiester bond
amino acid	denaturation	antiparallel
peptide bond		

Textbook pp. 39–47

MAIN IDEA: Amino acids are the monomer building blocks of proteins. There are 20 different amino acids. They all contain an amino group, a carboxyl group, and an R-group. The R-group gives each amino acid its unique characteristics.

1. In **Figure 1**, add the amino group, carboxyl group, and hydrogen atom to each amino acid. Circle the R-group in each amino acid. K/U

(a) Alanine   (b) Cysteine   (c) Aspartic acid

Figure 1

> **LEARNING TIP**
>
> **R-Groups**
> Create a chart of the different R-groups, their chemical components, and their properties.

2. (a) Explain the function of the R-group in an amino acid.

   (b) List the different types of amino acids. K/U

MAIN IDEA: Proteins are complex polymers. They have primary, secondary, tertiary, and quaternary levels of structure, which contribute to their functions. Some proteins require non-protein components, called prosthetic groups, to function properly.

3. Order the following elements of protein from simplest to most complex: protein, peptide, polypeptide, R-group, amino acid. T/I

4. Each diagram in **Figure 2** below shows one level of organization of a protein. Identify each level and describe it. K/U T/I

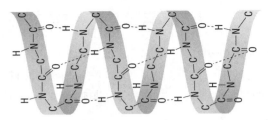

(a) _____

_____

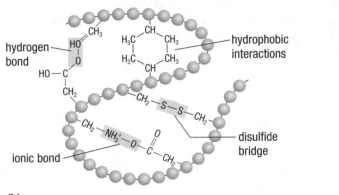

(b) _____

_____

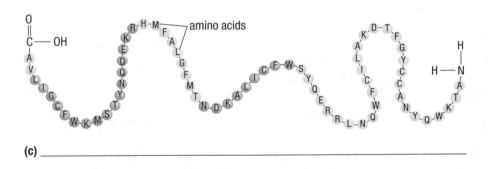

(c) _____

_____

Figure 2

5. Hemoglobin is made up of four polypeptides, but also require a heme group to transport oxygen. Describe the heme groups and explain their function. K/U T/I

MAIN IDEA: Nucleic acids, DNA, and RNA carry instructions for and help assemble all proteins that are produced in the cells. DNA and RNA are polymers of nucleotides. All nucleotides consist of three parts; a nitrogenous base, a five-carbon sugar, and one to three phosphates.

6. Which nucleic acid, DNA or RNA, performs each function? K/U

   (a) Helps with protein synthesis in a cell. _____

   (b) Stores information responsible for all inherited traits in all eukaryotes and prokaryotes. _____

   (c) Stores information responsible for all inherited traits in some viruses.

   _____

7. Label the three main parts of a nucleic acid in **Figure 3**. K/U

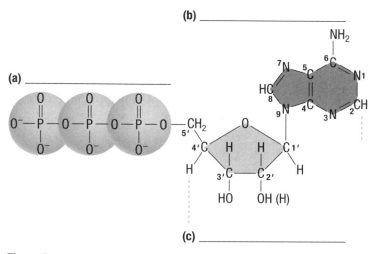

Figure 3

8. Every nucleotide contains one of five types of nitrogenous base. List each type of nitrogenous base in the correct category. K/U

   (a) Pyrimidines (one organic ring) _____

   (b) Purines (two-ringed) _____

9. (a) Label each nitrogenous base in the double strand of DNA in **Figure 4**.

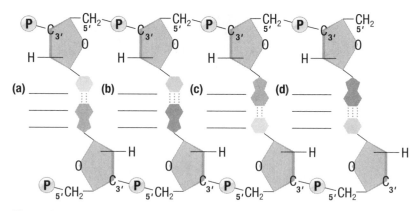

Figure 4

   (b) Figure 4 above shows a phosphodiester bond. Explain what this is. K/U

Textbook pp. 48–49

Linus Pauling: Creativity and Controversy in Science and Society

MAIN IDEA: With creativity, and considerable research, Linus Pauling was instrumental in discovering and describing many foundational elements of modern molecular biology. While much of his work is now accepted as important and true, some of his efforts were seen at the time as controversial, and some still are.

1. Linus Pauling was active in several areas of science. List four areas in which he made a lasting impression. K/U

2. Describe two of Linus Pauling's discoveries about biological molecules and bonding. Explain how each discovery helped develop the scientific understandings included in this chapter. T/I

3. What are the main differences between Linus Pauling's conclusions about proteins that led to his Nobel Prize in Chemistry and his conclusions about megadoses of vitamins. T/I

4. To what degree do you think Linus Pauling's status as a respected scientist contributed to the U.S. government's sanctions against him for his stance against nuclear arms? T/I

Enzymes

Vocabulary

enzyme	cofactor	allosteric site
substrate	coenzyme	allosteric regulation
active site	competitive inhibition	feedback inhibition
induced-fit model	noncompetitive inhibition	

Textbook pp. 50–57

MAIN IDEA: An enzyme is a biological catalyst with a specific three-dimensional shape, which is necessary for its function. The active site of an enzyme is specific to a particular substrate(s).

1. Why does a typical cell require about 4000 different enzymes to carry out its functions? K/U

2. Describe the "induced-fit hypothesis" for enzyme binding that allows an enzyme to catalyze reactions efficiently. T/I

3. **Figure 1** shows a reaction catalyzed by an enzyme. Describe what is happening at each step. C

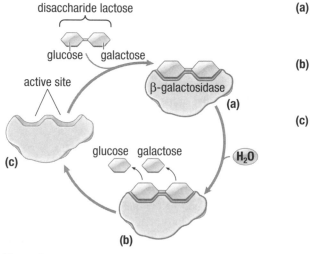

(a)

(b)

(c)

Figure 1

4. Compare and contrast cofactors and coenzymes. T/I

MAIN IDEA: Enzyme activity is affected by substrate and enzyme concentrations, temperature, and pH.

5. Sketch a graph to show how the rate of reaction changes in each situation. K/U

(a) enzyme concentration increases with a constant high concentration of substrate

(b) substrate concentration increases with a constant intermediate concentration of enzyme

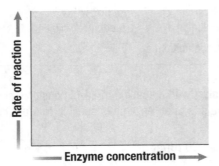

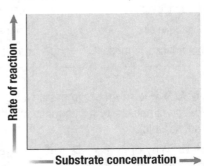

6. Consider **Figure 2**, which shows the effect of temperature on enzyme activity. K/U C

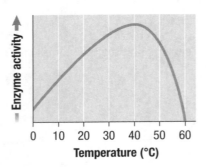

Figure 2

(a) What causes enzyme activity to increase between 0 °C and 40 °C?

(b) What causes enzyme activity to decrease above 40 °C?

(c) Do all enzymes exhibit peak activity at 40 °C? Explain.

MAIN IDEA: Competitive inhibitors enter an enzyme's active site to block the binding of the substrate. Noncompetitive inhibitors attach to another site on the enzyme, which changes the shape of the enzyme and its affinity for the substrate. Allosteric regulation of enzymes can inhibit or stimulate enzyme activity by altering the affinity of the active site for the substrate.

7. Classify penicillin as a competitive inhibitor or a noncompetitive inhibitor. Describe how it functions to inhibit enzyme activity. T/I

8. Compare and contrast the mechanism and effects of allosteric regulation and noncompetitive inhibition of enzyme activity. [T/I]

MAIN IDEA: Biochemical pathways often involve feedback inhibition as a mechanism for regulating the pathway. In negative feedback inhibition, an enzyme involved at the beginning of the pathway is inhibited by a product in the pathway.

9. Draw a flow chart to show the steps in the process of feedback inhibition. [K/U] [C]

10. Why is feedback inhibition so important for the efficient functioning of cells? [T/I]

MAIN IDEA: There are many industrial and commercial uses of enzymes, including the processing of starch, the production of cheese, and their addition to cleaning products as additives.

11. Think of seven industrial or commercial processes that use enzymes. Then use **Table 1** to classify how the enzyme is used in each process. [T/I]

Table 1 Enzyme Functions

Eliminate a reactant or create a product	Make a process faster or more efficient

12. Lactose intolerance may be a problem for some people. Describe what is it and how enzymes are involved. [T/I] [A]

The Biochemical Basis of Life

You have learned about biochemical components of cells and their functions. Use the flow charts to summarize what you have learned in this chapter. Add more parts to flow charts to help you.

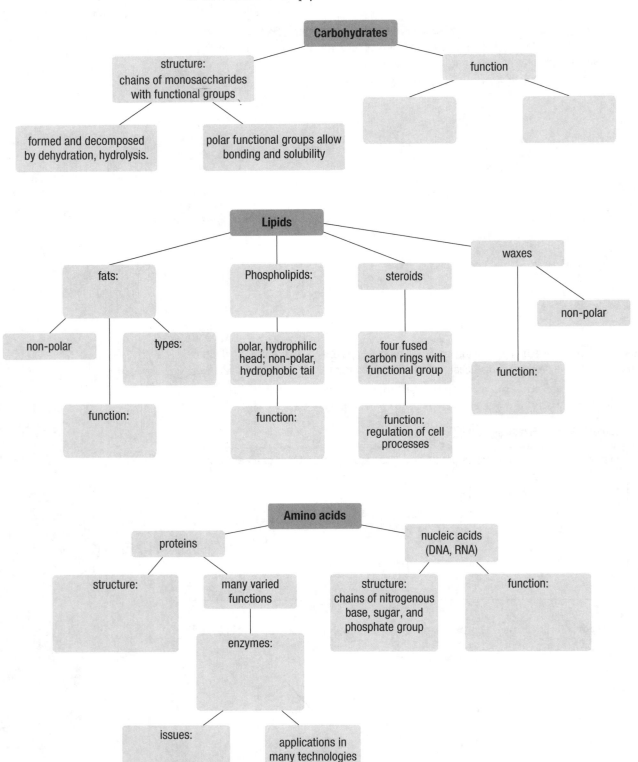

1. Which is a result of hydrogen bonding? (1.1) K/U
   (a) monosaccharides form long chains to become polysaccharides
   (b) radioactivity
   (c) H_2 is formed
   (d) the surface tension of water

2. Which pairs of nitrogenous bases bond with each other in DNA? (1.5) K/U
   (a) adenine and cytosine; guanine and thymine
   (b) adenine and thymine; cytosine and guanine
   (c) adenine and uracil; cytosine and guanine
   (d) adenine and guanine; cytosine and thymine

3. Indicate whether each statement is true or false. If you think the statement is false, rewrite it to make it true. K/U
   (a) The main function of protein is tissue development, especially muscle tissue. (1.5)

   (b) Complex carbohydrates and fatty acids both have backbones made of hydrocarbon chains. (1.4)

   (c) If a group of atoms contains a hydroxyl group, then groups of atoms is an aldehyde. (1.3)

4. Use the properties of valence electrons to explain why helium and neon are not very reactive elements. (1.1) T/I

5. Contrast a strong acid or base with a weak acid or base. (1.2) K/U T/I

6. What is the role of a functional group on a group of atoms? (1.3) K/U

7. How does the amphipathic nature of phospholipids help them perform their role in membranes? (1.4) T/I

K/U Knowledge and Understanding
T/I Thinking and Investigating
C Communication
A Application

8. Most enzymes function most effectively at a pH close to 7. Pepsin functions best at a pH of 1.5. What does this enable pepsin to do? (1.7) A

9. Which mechanism is the most efficient for feedback inhibition: reversible inhibition or irreversible inhibition? Why? (1.7) T/I A

10. Draw a diagram to show how polar molecules dissolve in water. (1.2) T/I C

11. Draw a diagram to show the reaction that occurs as two monosaccharides bond to create a polysaccharide. What type of reaction is this? (1.4) K/U C

12. Complete **Table 1** to summarize the primary characteristics of the major biological molecules. (1.4, 1.5, 1.7) T/I

Table 1 Characteristics of Biological Molecules

	Components	Reactions	Functions
Carbohydrates			
Lipids			
Proteins			
Nucleic Acids			

Cell Structures

Vocabulary

organelle	rough ER	plastid	cilia
plasma membrane	smooth ER	chloroplast	cell wall
nuclear envelope	vesicle	chromoplast	primary wall
endomembrane system	vacuole	amyloplast	secondary wall
endoplasmic reticulum (ER)	lysosome	cytoskeleton	extracellular matrix (ECM)
	Golgi body	microfilament	cell junction
	mitochondrion	flagellum	

Textbook pp. 72–80

MAIN IDEA: Eukaryotic cells have many different internal compartments, called organelles. Each organelle has a specific role in various cellular activities.

1. Why do cellular organelles have so many different shapes? K/U

   because they do different tasks

2. Complete **Table 1** to summarize the function of organelles found in eukaryotic cells. K/U C

   Table 1 The Function of Organelles in Eukaryotic Cells

Organelle	Function
nucleus	· contains DNA
nucleolus	· ribosomes are assembled from RNA
endoplasmic reticulum (ER)	· modifies proteins + lipids · transports them in vesicles to golgi.
Golgi body	· packages + ships proteins throughout cell / body
vesicle	· carry proteins + lipids between organelles
mitochondrion	· converts food molecules into ATP
plastid	· where photosynthesis occurs · chloroplast + storage

LEARNING TIP

Cytoplasm versus Cytosol
The term "cytoplasm" is often used to refer to the liquid portion of the cell, but the more precise term is "cytosol." Cell biologists use "cytoplasm" to refer to all the internal components of the cell other than the nucleus.

MAIN IDEA: Plant cells and animal cells have many of the same organelles. Plant cells also have a cell wall, plastids, and a large central vacuole.

3. Would animal cells function better if they had central vacuoles and cell walls? Explain. T/I

   no, b/c animal cells have cytoskeleton for structure and other vacuoles for storage vesicles

4. Sketch a diagram of a plant cell and an animal cell. Label the parts to show how the two types of cells are similar. K/U T/I C

MAIN IDEA: Eukaryotic cells have an extensive and dynamic framework called a cytoskeleton. The cytoskeleton is used for cell shape, internal structure, movement, and cell division. Many cells are surrounded by and supported by a complex extracellular matrix and are able to interact with adjacent cells and the environment via cell junctions.

5. List three common components of microtubules and microfilaments. K/U

· tubulin

· actin

· myosin

6. Complete the paragraph to describe how organelles help cells and cell contents move around. K/U

_____Microtubules_____ help to move cell components, such as a cell's duplicated ___chromosomes___ during cell division. They rapidly assemble when needed and then disassemble. ___microfilaments___ strengthen and change the shape of a eukaryotic cell. In this way they can help the cell move. Organized arrays of ___microtubules___ are found in ___cilia___ and ___flagella___ of eukaryotic cells. Elongated ___microfilaments___ in amoebas' ___pseudopods___, or false feet, help these single-celled organisms move.

7. Describe four examples of extracellular matrix in different organisms. K/U

Membrane Structure and Functions

Textbook pp. 81–86

Vocabulary

fluid mosaic model	glycoprotein	integral membrane protein
glycolipid	sterol	peripheral membrane protein

MAIN IDEA: A biological membrane consists of a bilayer of phospholipids and proteins which move around freely within the layer. This is described as the fluid mosaic model.

1. What are the main functions of membranes in cells? K/U

2. What function of normal membranes is impaired in the cells of people with cystic fibrosis? What problems does this cause? T/I

3. Identify the component parts of the plasma membrane shown in **Figure 1**. K/U

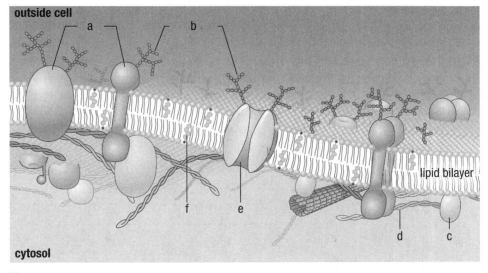

Figure 1

(a) _____   (d) _____

(b) _____   (e) _____

(c) _____   (f) _____

> **STUDY TIP**
>
> **Complex Diagrams**
> At first a complex diagram may seem confusing but repeated examinations and relabelling the diagram will help you become familiar with the parts. After becoming familiar with the diagram, it will not seem so complicated.

4. What characteristics of phospholipid molecules cause them to form a membrane with two layers? Sketch a diagram to help you explain. K/U C

MAIN IDEA: The fluidity of a plasma membrane depends on the composition of the lipid molecules that make up the membrane, as well as the temperature. Membranes contain sterols, which help to maintain their fluidity.

5. Which form a more rigid lipid bilayer: lipids containing mostly saturated fatty acids or lipids containing mostly unsaturated fatty acids? Explain. K/U T/I

6. Complete the following description of the role of sterols in a membrane. K/U

At high temperatures, sterols in a membrane help to_____
the movement of the lipids. At low temperatures, the sterols occupy

_____ between the _____ and prevent the fatty acids

from associating and forming a _____. In these ways, sterols

_____ the fluidity of a membrane at high temperatures and

_____ the fluidity of a membrane at low temperatures.

MAIN IDEA: Membrane proteins have four functions: transport, enzymatic activity, triggering signals and attachment and recognition of molecules. Membrane proteins may be embedded into the lipid bilayer (integral membrane proteins) or positioned on top of the lipid bilayer (peripheral membrane proteins).

7. Describe the function of the membrane protein in **Figure 2** to **Figure 5** and explain how the protein is carrying out its function. K/U C

(a)

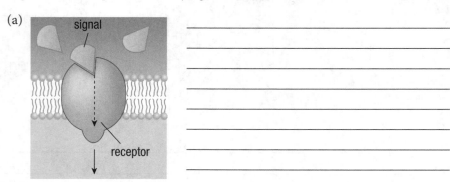

Figure 2

_____
_____
_____
_____
_____
_____
_____
_____
_____

(b)

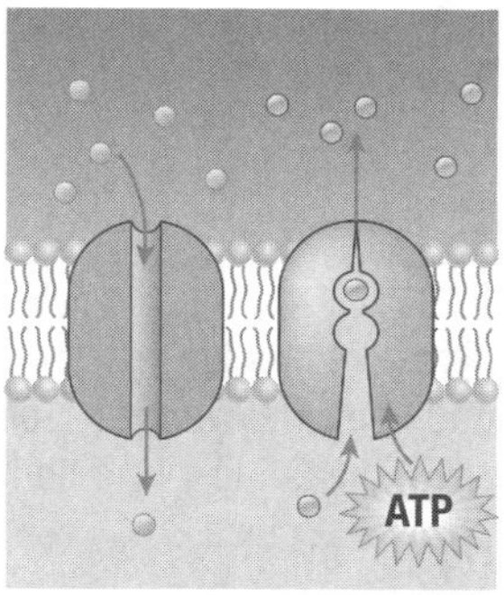

Figure 3

(c)

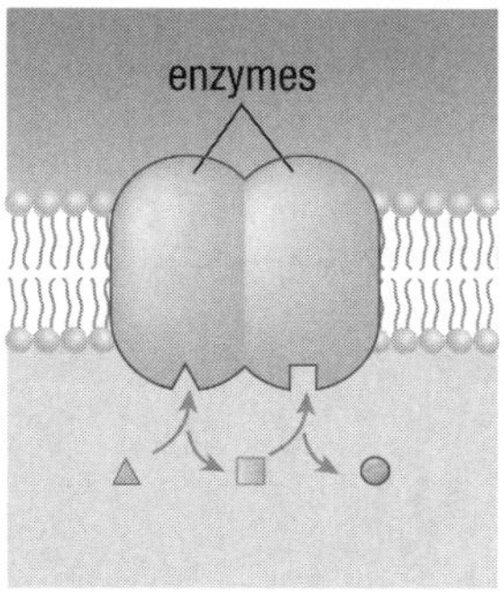

enzymes

Figure 4

(d)

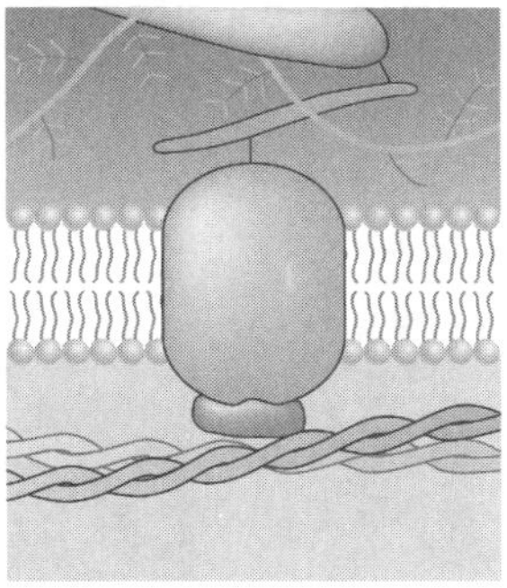

Figure 5

8. Which key membrane function or functions does each membrane protein in question 7 support? (Refer to your list of the main membrane functions in question 1.) T/I

(a)

(b)

(c)

(d)

9. Consider the membrane proteins in question 7. What cellular functions must always be performed by an integral membrane protein? Explain. T/I

Textbook pp. 87–88

LEARNING TIP

Researching on the Internet
Search the Internet for more information on nanotechnology and its application in areas other than medicine.

Nanotechnology in Medicine

MAIN IDEA: Scientists are researching ways to use nanotechnology in areas such as cancer research, cell and bone repair, gene therapy, and drug delivery. One of the main challenges is predicting how something this small will react once it is in the body.

1. Describe two areas in which nanotechnology is currently used. K/U

2. Describe two areas of current research in the field of nanotechnology. K/U

3. What ethical issues are researchers in the field of nanotechnology concerned about? T/I

4. Predict some applications of nanotechnology that may be in common use in five or ten years. T/I A

Transport across Membranes

Textbook pp. 89–97

Vocabulary

passive transport	channel protein	hypertonic
dynamic equilibrium	carrier protein	isotonic
simple diffusion	osmosis	active transport
facilitated diffusion	hypotonic	electrochemical gradient
transport protein		

MAIN IDEA: Cells and cell organelles must interact with their environment by allowing and controlling the inward and outward movement of molecules and ions through their membrane.

1. Explain what happens when a cell membrane encounters each type of molecule. K/U
   (a) a large food molecule _____
   (b) a waste molecule _____
   (c) a harmful foreign substance _____
   (d) a valuable molecule inside the cell _____

2. Fill in the blanks to complete the description of substances passing through mitochondria and chloroplast membranes in eukaryotic cells. K/U

   For vital chemical reactions to occur, _____ must cross the

   membrane into the organelle. Both _____ products, such as

   _____ and valuable products such as _____ must cross

   the membrane out of the organelle.

MAIN IDEA: Some molecules can pass through a membrane using passive transport (simple or facilitated diffusion), which depends on a concentration gradient. Osmosis is the passive diffusion of water across a membrane.

3. (a) What types of molecules diffuse across membranes unassisted?

   (b) What types of molecules do not diffuse across membranes on their own and require assistance? K/U

4. Consider the graph in **Figure 1**. Why is the rate of facilitated transport greater than the rate of simple diffusion? T/I

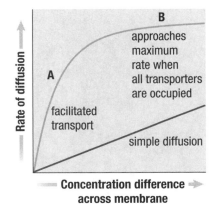

Figure 1

5. Match each condition with its description. K/U

(a) A cell in isotonic conditions

(b) A cell in hypotonic conditions

(c) A cell in hypertonic conditions

(i) Dissolved substances outside the cell are at higher concentrations than inside the cell.

(ii) Dissolved substances inside the cell are at higher concentrations than outside the cell.

(iii) Dissolved substances inside and outside the cell are at the same concentration.

MAIN IDEA: Active transport moves a substance against a concentration gradient across a membrane, using a pump. Primary active transport pumps include H^+, Ca^+, Na^+, and K^+ pumps. Secondary transport pumps occur via symport or antiport.

6. Complete each step to describe the process of primary active transport. K/U

Step 1: A transport protein binds with a(n) _____ group from ATP. This provides energy.

Step 2: The _____ of the transport protein changes to readily bind a(n) _____.

Step 3: A(n) _____ binds to the binding site.

Step 4: The transport protein folds to expose the ion to the _____ side of the membrane and _____ its binding strength.

Step 5: The ion is _____ and the protein reverts to its original shape.

7. Sketch a diagram to show each type of secondary active transport. Include arrows to show the direction of the ions and solutes. K/U C

(a) symport

(b) antiport

MAIN IDEA: Endocytosis moves aggregate molecules into the cell. Exocytosis moves proteins and wastes out of the cell.

8. Explain what happens during the three phases of exocytosis. K/U

9. Describe what happens during each type of endocytosis. K/U

(a) bulk-phase endocytosis

(b) receptor-mediated endocytosis

(c) phagocytosis

Cell Structure and Function

Summarize what you have learned about cell structure and function. Complete the concept map and add more information to help you understand the functions of cell components and processes carried out within cells.

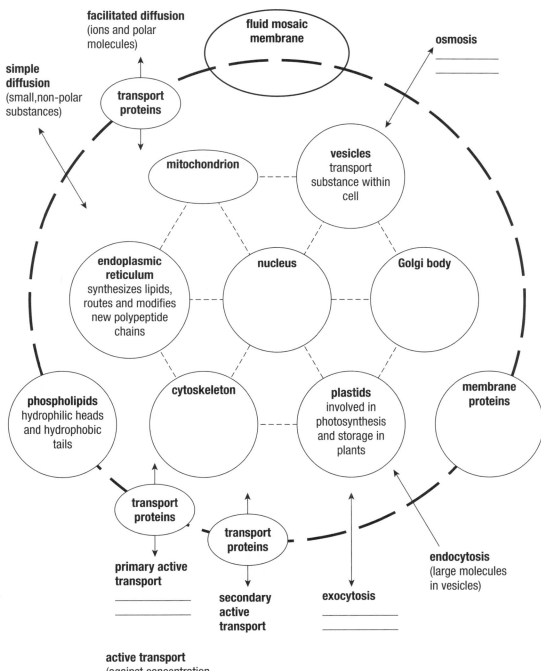

passive transport
(with concentration gradient)

facilitated diffusion
(ions and polar molecules)

fluid mosaic membrane

osmosis
_____
_____

simple diffusion
(small,non-polar substances)

transport proteins

mitochondrion

vesicles
transport substance within cell

endoplasmic reticulum
synthesizes lipids, routes and modifies new polypeptide chains

nucleus

Golgi body

phospholipids
hydrophilic heads and hydrophobic tails

cytoskeleton

plastids
involved in photosynthesis and storage in plants

membrane proteins

transport proteins

transport proteins

primary active transport
_____
_____

secondary active transport

exocytosis
_____
_____

endocytosis
(large molecules in vesicles)

active transport
(against concentration gradient)

K/U Knowledge and Understanding
T/I Thinking and Investigating
C   Communication
A   Application

1. What substance forms the basic structure of cilia and flagella in eukaryotes? (2.1) K/U
   (a) chitin
   (b) microtubules
   (c) mineral deposits
   (d) myocin microfilaments

2. In which process does a vesicle fuse with the cell membrane and then release its contents outside the cell? (2.4) K/U
   (a) facilitated diffusion
   (b) passive transport
   (c) endocytosis
   (d) exocytosis

3. Indicate whether each statement is true or false. If you think the statement is false, rewrite it to make it true. K/U
   (a) A cell's mitochondria is mainly responsible for protein synthesis. (2.1)

   (b) In a phospholipid bilayer membrane, phospholipid molecules arrange themselves in two layers with hydrophilic ends facing out and their hydrophobic ends facing one another in the middle. (2.2)

4. Explain the functions of the three types of plastids in plant cells. (2.1) K/U

5. A particular membrane protein includes no hydrophobic amino acids. Is this protein an integral membrane protein or a peripheral membrane protein? How do you know? (2.2) A

6. Researchers may one day develop nanotechnology that synthesizes polypeptide chains when a person's smooth ER is not able to do so. What do you thinks are some of the benefits and risks associated with this nanotechnology? (2.1, 2.3) T/I A

7. Sketch a fluid mosaic model of a plasma membrane. Label your diagram. (2.2) K/U

8. Explain what happens during the three phases of simple diffusion. (2.4) K/U C

9. Complete **Table 1** to compare active transport to passive transport. (2.4) T/I

Table 1 Passive Transport versus Active Transport

	Passive transport (simple diffusion)	Passive transport (facilitated diffusion)	Active transport
Direction of transport			
Energy source			
Membrane component that enables transport			

1. Which type of molecule has a long hydrocarbon backbone? (1.3) K/U
   (a) fatty acids
   (b) ions
   (c) amino acids
   (d) DNA

2. What characteristic of phospholipids makes them suitable for forming cell membranes? (2.2) K/U
   (a) They form strong bonds with other molecules.
   (b) They have active sites that can bind to a substrate.
   (c) They have hydrophilic ends and hydrophobic ends, helping them control what passes through the membrane.
   (d) They are most active at high temperatures.

3. Indicate whether each statement is true or false. If you think the statement is false, rewrite it to make it true. K/U
   (a) Proteins are long chains of up to 20 different amino acids. (1.5)

   (b) The endomembrane system consists of the cell membrane and transport proteins. (2.1)

4. Describe what an extracellular matrix is and give two examples. (2.1) K/U T/I

5. (a) What function do enzymes perform?

   (b) Describe two examples of the commercial use of enzymes. (1.7) K/U

6. How do vesicles and Golgi bodies work together in a cell? (2.1) K/U A

7. Draw a Lewis dot diagram for each element. (1.1) C
   (a) helium   (b) carbon   (c) nitrogen

8. Draw diagrams to show the four levels of protein structure. (1.5) [C]

9. Explain what happens during each type of enzyme inhibition.
   Draw diagrams to help you. (1.7) [K/U] [C]
   (a) competitive inhibition

   (b) noncompetitive inhibition

10. Use **Table 1** to compare the structure and function of the main components
    of a cell membrane. (2.2) [T/I]

    Table 1 Cell Membrane Structure and Function

	Role	Hydrophilic or hydrophobic
phospholipids		
integral membrane proteins		
peripheral membrane proteins		
sterols		

11. Explain what happens during the three phases of endocytosis. (2.4) [K/U]

Metabolic Processes

BIG IDEAS

- All metabolic processes involve chemical changes and energy conversions.

- An understanding of metabolic processes enables people to make informed choices with respect to a range of personal, societal, and environmental issues.

Chapter 3: An Introduction to Metabolism

Energy is defined as the capacity to do work. All living things need a constant supply of energy. Energy cannot be created nor destroyed; only transformed or transferred. However, some energy is lost in every transfer, leaving the remaining free energy available to do work. The energy that is not lost, or the portion that is still available to do work in the given system, is called free energy. The free energy value of a chemical reaction (ΔG) provides us with useful information in the study of metabolism.

Cells require energy to carry out life processes. ATP supplies energy directly to chemical reactions in all cells. ATP hydrolysis results in the formation of ADP and P_i, and releases a large amount of free energy in the process.

Chemical reactions require activation energy to initiate the breaking of bonds in reactants. The spontaneity of a reaction does not predict how fast it will occur. Some spontaneous reactions are very slow. Enzymes speed up reactions by lowering the activation energy of the reaction. Potential energy that is stored in food molecules is released during oxidation reactions.

Chapter 4: Cellular Respiration

Cellular respiration is a series of metabolic reactions within cells to convert energy stored in nutrients to usable energy. There are three main types of energy pathways: aerobic respiration, anaerobic respiration, and fermentation. They all produce ATP.

Respiration pathways use electron transport systems to generate ATP by oxidative phosphorylation. Fermentation pathways enable organisms to use glycolysis as a source of ATP, without an electron transport chain. Anaerobic respiration uses an inorganic substance other than oxygen as the final oxidizing agent. Fermentation relies on an organic compound.

Chapter 5: Photosynthesis: The Energy of Life

Photosynthesis is a process by which producers convert light energy into chemical energy. This chemical energy is then stored and used to assemble energy-rich organic molecules that are used by both producers and consumers. Photosynthesis has two stages: the light-dependent reactions and the light-independent reactions (the Calvin cycle).

Aerobic cellular respiration and photosynthesis form a cycle. Some of the products of one process serve as the reactants for the other process and vice versa. Photosynthesis occurs in the chloroplasts of cells, while part of aerobic cellular respiration occurs in the mitochondria. Plants and most other producers perform both photosynthesis and aerobic cellular respiration. Most consumers perform aerobic cellular respiration. However they must rely on producers for the synthesis of the organic molecules they use as energy and as building materials for growth.

Metabolism and Energy

Textbook pp. 126–140

Vocabulary

metabolism	activation energy	spontaneous change
kinetic energy	transition state	free energy
potential energy	exothermic reaction	exergonic reaction
first law of thermodynamics	endothermic reaction	endergonic reaction
bond energy	second law of thermodynamics	energy coupling
mole	entropy	catabolic pathway
		anabolic pathway

MAIN IDEA: The first law of thermodynamics states that energy transforms from one form to another or transfers from one object to another, but it is neither created nor destroyed. The second law of thermodynamics states that in every transfer and conversion of energy, there is less energy available to do work. The total entropy of a system and its surroundings always increases.

1. Give an example of the first and second laws of thermodynamics. Explain how your examples relate to each law. K/U T/I

   ① food is eaten, then broken down to energy and used for kinetic purposes

   ② Entropy ~ disorder happens spontaneously (messy room), order requires energy (clean room)

2. Distinguish between kinetic energy and potential energy. Give an example of potential energy being transformed into kinetic energy. K/U A

   kinetic: occurs as a result of motion

   potential: stored within an object; food → when bonds break, energy released.

MAIN IDEA: During a chemical reaction, bonds in the reactants break and bonds in the products form. For the bonds in the reactants to break, energy must be absorbed. As bonds form, energy is released.

3. When ethane gas, C_2H_6, burns, carbon dioxide gas, CO_2, and water, H_2O are formed. The following chemical equation describes this reaction.

$$2 C_2H_6 + 7 O_2 \rightarrow 4 CO_2 + 6 H_2O$$

(a) Create and label a diagram of the reaction. Colour the bonds between the atoms that are broken in red and the bonds between atoms that are formed in blue.

   $2C_2H_6 + 7O_2 \rightarrow 4CO_2 + 6H_2O$

(b) Describe the changes in energy as bonds are broken and formed. K/U C

   broken = require energy

   formed = release in energy.

4. Label **Figure 1** (a) and (b) with the following words: activation energy, transition state, net amount of energy released during bond formation, net amount of energy released, net amount of energy absorbed. K/U C

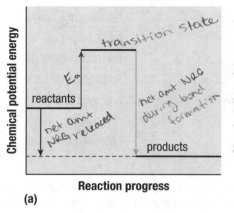

Exothermic Reaction

Chemical potential energy vs *Reaction progress*

Ea
reactants
transition state
net amt NRG released
net amt NRG during bond formation
products

(a)

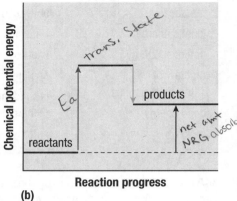

Endothermic Reaction

Chemical potential energy vs *Reaction progress*

trans. State
Ea
products
reactants
net amt NRG absorbed

(b)

Figure 1

5. Define each of the following terms in your own words. Give an example from everyday life. K/U C A

(a) activation energy:

the minimum amt of NRG required to start a reaction

(b) transition state:

a temporary state where the reactant bonds are breaking and the product bonds form.

(c) exothermic reaction:

an overall net release of energy (products have less chem. potential NRG)

(d) endothermic reaction:

an overall net absorption of energy. (products have more chem. potential NRG)

6. (a) Calculate the energy released per gram of sucrose when it is burned in a combustion reaction. The chemical formula for sucrose is $C_{12}H_{22}O_{11}$. Include a structural diagram for the reaction.

Combustion = products – reactants

Table 1 Average Bond Energies

Bond type	Average bond energy (kJ/mol)
H—H	436
C—H	411
O—H	459
N—H	391
C—C	346
C—O	359
C=O	799
O=O	494

(b) Is the reaction exothermic or endothermic? Explain. K/U T/I C

MAIN IDEA: Gibbs free energy (G) is the energy in a system that is still available to do work after a reaction occurs. Exergonic reactions have a negative ΔG value, are spontaneous, and release free energy. Endergonic reactions have a positive ΔG value, are not spontaneous, and absorb free energy. They must be coupled with an exergonic reaction to proceed.

7. Does spontaneous change mean that some chemical reactions randomly begin on their own? Explain. K/U

no, spontaneous change still needs some sort of ignition, but once started, the reaction will continue on its own.

8. Describe each of the following terms in your own words. Give an example of each. K/U T/I C

(a) Gibbs free energy

The energy that is not lost during a transformation. Ex. the oxidation of glucose releases free energy.

(b) exergonic reaction

a reaction that has a net release of energy, (-ve ΔG), spontaneous
* products have less free energy

(c) endergonic reaction

a reaction that has a net gain of energy, (+ve ΔG), not spontaneous
* products have more free energy

9. Draw a table to summarize the energy changes involved in the following reactions: exothermic change, endothermic change, exergonic reaction, and endergonic reaction. K/U C

10. Define "coupled reactions" in your own words. K/U C

When an exergonic reaction is paired with an endergonic reaction → feed off each other

→ NRG from exergonic makes endergonic occur

→ net -ve ΔG, occur spontaneously

MAIN IDEA: Metabolic pathways are a series of chemical reactions. Catabolic pathways result in an overall decrease in free energy—free energy is released. Anabolic pathways result in an overall increase in free energy—free energy is absorbed.

11. Complete the following summary of anabolic and catabolic pathways. K/U

In a(n) _____catabolic_____ pathway, _____complex_____ molecules are broken down into _____simple_____ molecules. Free energy is _____released_____. In a(n) _____anabolic_____ pathway, _____simple_____ molecules are _____built_____ into _____complex_____ molecules. Free energy is _____absorbed_____.

12. Define "anabolic pathway" in your own words. K/U C

energy is supplied to build complex molecules. Net ΔG is +ve

13. Use **Table 1** to list examples of chemical reactions involved in metabolism that are catabolic or anabolic. K/U T/I

Table 1 Catabolic and Anabolic Reactions

Catabolic reaction	Anabolic reaction
• cellular respiration	• photosynthesis • synthesis of macromolecules

ATP: Energy Currency of the Cell

> **Vocabulary**
>
> phosphorylation   ATP cycle

MAIN IDEA: ATP supplies energy directly to chemical reactions in all cells. It is the universal energy currency in living organisms. ATP supplies the energy that powers nearly every activity of a cell.

1. Identify each part of the ATP molecule in **Figure 1**. K/U C

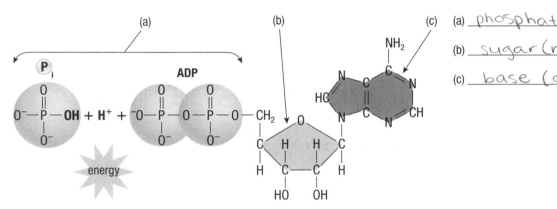

(a) _phosphate group_

(b) _sugar (ribose)_

(c) _base (adenine)_

Figure 1

2. In **Table 1**, list an example of the use of ATP energy for each type of work. K/U C

   Table 1 Use of ATP Energy

Type of work	Example
Mechanical	contraction of muscles
Transport	pump substances across membrane against concentration gradient.
Chemical	supply chem. potential NRG for endergonic reactions (DNA replication)

> **LEARNING TIP**
>
> **Phosphate abbreviation**
> The PO_3OH molecule (phosphate) is an inorganic form of phosphorus and an essential component of ATP. It is symbolized P_i.

MAIN IDEA: ATP hydrolysis results in the formation of ADP and P_i, and releases a large amount of free energy in the process. ATP hydrolysis can be coupled to endergonic reactions in a cell to power hundreds of reactions.

3. Write the chemical equation that describes ATP hydrolysis. K/U C

$$ATP + H_2O \rightarrow ADP + P_i \quad (\Delta G = -30.5 \text{ kJ/mol})$$

4. Complete the following description of ATP hydrolysis and the energy of this reaction. K/U

In ATP hydrolysis, the ___energy___ that is released from the ___addition___ of water is used by cells to ___start___ another reaction. This transfer of ___energy___ from one reaction to another to drive the second reaction is called ___reaction coupling___.

5. Why is ATP the energy source mainly used by cells? **K/U** **T/I**

because it contains large amounts of free energy (due to -vely charged P groups)

MAIN IDEA: ATP is regenerated from ADP and P_i during part of the ATP cycle.

6. In **Figure 2**, fill in the blanks to descibe how energy is produced in the ATP cycle. **K/U** **C**

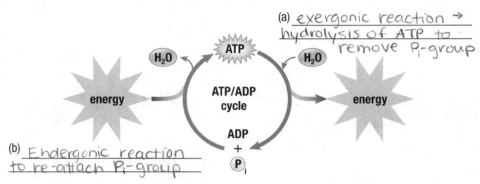

(a) *exergonic reaction → hydrolysis of ATP to remove P_i-group*

(b) *Endergonic reaction to re-attach P_i-group*

Figure 2

7. The following is an example of a coupled reaction. **K/U** **T/I**
   (a) Write the term "energy" on the proper side of each equation.

   $ATP + H_2O$ _____ → $ADP + P_i$ + _*energy*_

   relaxed muscle + _*energy*_ → contracted muscle + _____

   (b) Give reasons for your choices.

8. In the first reaction in the metabolism of glucose, glucose undergoes phosphorylation to produce glucose-6-phosphate as shown. **K/U** **T/I** **C** **A**
   (a) Complete the free energy calculations.
   (b) Label each reaction as endergonic or exergonic.
   (c) Write an equation for the net or resultant reaction.
   (d) Indicate whether or not the coupled reaction is spontaneous or non-spontaneous. Explain.

   glucose + P_i → glucose-6-phosphate + H_2O $\Delta G = +13.8$ kJ/mol (*endergonic*)

   $ATP + H_2O → ADP + P_i$ $\Delta G =$ _*-30.5*_ (*exergonic*)

   net $\Delta G =$ _*- 16.7*_

   Net reaction:

   Spontaneous, because net reaction is

   glucose + ATP → glucose-6-phosphate + ADP *-ΔG*

Enzymes and Activation Energy

MAIN IDEA: An activation energy barrier must be overcome for any reaction to proceed. Activation energy initiates the breaking of bonds in reactants as they reach the transition state.

Textbook pp. 146–150

1. Use the example of a match starting a fire to explain the concept of activation energy. K/U T/I C

2. Give an everyday example of overcoming an activation barrier. Identify the reactants and the products in **Figure 1** to illustrate your example. K/U T/I A

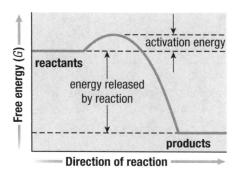

Figure 1

MAIN IDEA: Enzymes catalyze reactions by lowering the activation energy of the reaction. Enzymes can bring reactants to the transition state by one of three different mechanisms:
   1. bringing the two reactants closer together,
   2. changing the charged environment around the substrate,
   3. bending or distorting the substrate.

3. Is each statement true or false? If you think the statement is false, rewrite it to make it true. K/U

   (a) Enzymes increase the rate of a non-spontaneous reaction.

   F

   (b) Enzymes alter the reactants of a reaction.

   F

   (c) Enzymes do not supply free energy to a reaction.

   T

4. Explain the three mechanisms enzymes use to bring reactants to the transition state in **Table 1** below. K/U

Table 1 Enzyme Mechanisms

	Action of Enzyme on Substrate	Diagram
Mechanism 1	bring substrates together to break old and form new bonds	
Mechanism 2	bring substrates into charged environment to alter substrate	
Mechanism 3	distort/bend shape of substrate → weakens bonds	

5. How does the formation of the enzyme-subtrate complex explain the reduction of the activation energy of chemical reactions? T/I

Food as Fuel

Vocabulary		Textbook pp. 151–155
dehydrogenase	NADH	

MAIN IDEA: Oxidation refers to the loss of electrons, and reduction refers to the gain of electrons. Potential energy that is stored in food molecules is released during oxidation reactions.

1. In **Figure 1**, show the movement of electrons from one level to another using arrows. Explain what is occurring. K/U C

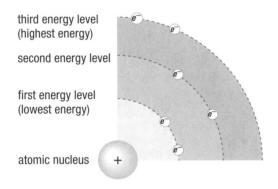

third energy level (highest energy)

second energy level

first energy level (lowest energy)

atomic nucleus +

Figure 1

2. Complete the following description of how energy is obtained from food molecules: Fats and carbohydrates in foods contain many bonds between _____C_____ and _____H_____ atoms. The __electrons__ in these bonds are in a(n) ____high____ energy state and are more strongly attracted to a(n) ____O____ atom. In a(n) __oxidation__ reaction, when the _____C–H_____ bond is broken and a(n) ____O–H____ bond is formed instead, ____energy____ is released. K/U

STUDY **TIP**

Using Mnemomics
Use word memory aids to help you remember definitions.
Oxidation could be OLE—Oxidation is loss of electrons.
Reduction could be RAGE—Reduction a gain of electrons.

3. Why does an oxidation reaction always occur together with a reduction reaction? K/U T/I

4. Which atom loses electrons in each oxidation reaction? K/U
   (a) glucose + oxygen → carbon dioxide + water _____
   (b) iron + oxygen → iron(III) oxide (rust) _____

5. (a) In the oxidation of methane, carbon dioxide and water are produced as shown in **Figure 2**. Describe what is happening by labelling the diagram.

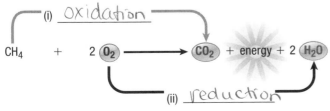

(i) __oxidation__

CH_4 + 2 O_2 ⟶ CO_2 + energy + 2 H_2O

(ii) __reduction__

Figure 2

(b) Explain what happens to the electrons in the C—H bonds of CH_4. K/U T/I C

MAIN IDEA: Rapid oxidation reactions lead to a rapid loss of energy in the form of waste thermal energy. Controlled oxidation reactions involve many steps. There is less waste energy because more released energy can be captured effectively.

6. Suggest two consequences to the cell if the rate of energy release from glucose could not be controlled. K/U T/I

7. Compare rapid combustion with controlled oxidation using a table. Which reaction would be beneficial for the metabolic reactions in a cell? Explain. K/U C

controled oxidation.

MAIN IDEA: During many cellular redox reactions, dehydrogenases facilitate the transfer of electrons from food to energy-carrier molecules. NAD^+ is a common high-energy electron carrier molecule in cellular processes, which is reduced to the form NADH. NADH provides a source of energy to drive ATP synthesis.

8. Outline two methods that are used by cells to control the rate of energy release from glucose. K/U

9. In **Figure 3**, label the arrow to indicate the direction of a reduction and the direction of an oxidation for this chemical reaction. K/U

$$NAD^+ + 2\,e^- + H^+ \rightleftharpoons NADH$$

(a) reduction
(b) oxidation

Figure 3

10. Based on the way in which NAD^+ functions, would you classify this molecule as an enzyme? Explain your thinking. K/U T/I

no,

An Introduction to Metabolism

In the chemical reactions of metabolic processes, energy is absorbed and energy is released. As shown in the concept map below, the absorption and release of energy affects cell metabolism.

In the concept map, list terms associated with adding energy to cells for metabolism and the terms associated with the release or loss of energy from metabolism. For each transfer of energy, think about the effect it has on cell metabolism. For example, energy from ATP is used to perform most cell functions.

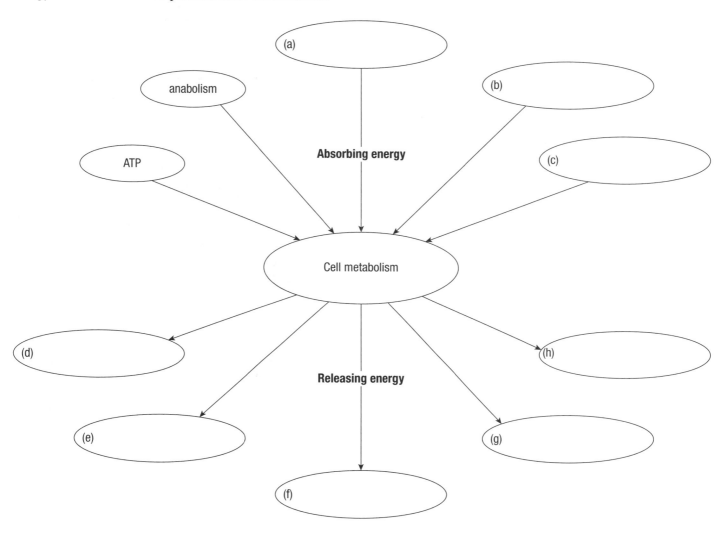

K/U Knowledge/Understanding
T/I Thinking/Investigation
C   Communication
A   Application

1. Plants are able to build glucose during photosynthesis. Which is the best description of this process? (3.1) K/U
   (a) catabolic, exothermic and endergonic
   (b) anabolic, endothermic and exergonic
   (c) catabolic, endothermic and endergonic
   (d) anabolic, endothermic and endergonic

2. Which equation correctly shows the hydrolysis of ATP? (3.2) K/U
   (a) $ATP + H_2O \rightarrow ADP + P_i$, $\Delta G = -30.5$ kJ/mol
   (b) $ATP + H_2O \rightarrow ADP + P_i$, $\Delta G = +30.5$ kJ/mol
   (c) $ATP + H_2O \rightarrow ADP + PO$ $\Delta G = -30.5$ kJ/mol
   (d) $ATP + H_2O \rightarrow ADP + P_i$, $\Delta G = 0$ kJ/mol

3. Which of the following statements about enzymes is true? (3.3) K/U
   (a) They are made of lipids and control the rate of chemical reactions.
   (b) They control the rate of chemical reactions by changing the temperature.
   (c) They catalyze reactions by increasing the activation energy.
   (d) They catalyze reactions by decreasing the activation energy.

4. Which of the following statements is true? (3.4) K/U
   (a) An electron absorbs energy if it moves closer to a large nucleus.
   (b) An electron releases energy if it moves closer to a large nucleus.
   (c) An electron absorbs energy when it moves to a lower energy level.
   (d) An electron releases energy when it moves to ha higher energy level.

5. Indicate whether each statement is true or false. If you think the statement is false, rewrite it to make it true. K/U
   (a) An exothermic reaction that involves an increase in entropy is spontaneous at all temperatures. (3.1)

   (b) Enzymes are biological catalysts that lower the energy required for a chemical reaction to occur. (3.3)

   (c) Temperature and pH affect enzyme activity by changing the shape of the enzymes. (3.3)

6. How can the laws of thermodynamics help explain how living things function? (3.1) K/U T/I A

7. Complete the following description of energy changes during a chemical reaction. (3.1) K/U

   All chemical reactions involve the _____ of energy as bonds

   break in the reactants and the _____ of energy as bonds

   form in the _____. In an exothermic reaction, the energy

   absorbed by _____ the bonds is _____ than the

   energy _____ by _____ the new bonds. In an

   _____ reaction the reverse is true.

8. Explain how an enzyme is able to catalyze the synthesis of a large molecule from two smaller molecules. Use a diagram to illustrate your answer. (3.3) K/U C

9. Use the ATP cycle as an example to explain the concepts of catabolism and anabolism. Provide a diagram to help you explain. (3.1) K/U T/I C

10. Explain the role of NAD^+ in the oxidation of food molecules. (3.4) K/U T/I

11. Fill in the bubble map by describing four industrial processes that make use of biological enzymes. (3.3) K/U T/I C A

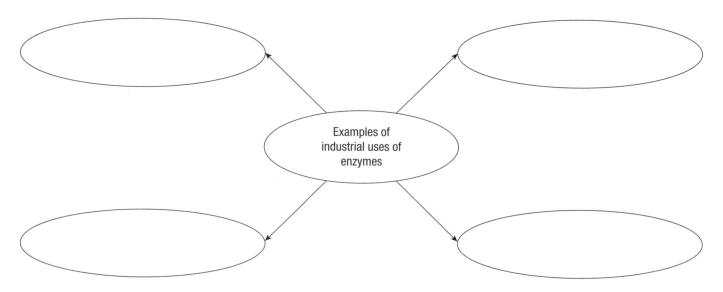

Introduction to Cellular Respiration and Fermentation

Textbook pp. 168–171

Vocabulary

aerobic cellular respiration	oxidative phosphorylation	anaerobic respiration
obligate aerobe	glycolysis	fermentation
substrate-level phosphorylation	pyruvate oxidation	obligate anaerobe
	citric acid cycle	facultative anaerobe

MAIN IDEA: There are three main types of respiratory pathways: aerobic respiration, anaerobic respiration, and fermentation. They all produce ATP. Mitochondria generate most of the ATP that is used in eukaryotic cells.

1. The energy that plants store in sugars, such as glucose, originally came from _____. K/U

2. The main purpose of cellular respiration is _____. K/U

3. Aerobic cellular respiration can only take place in the presence of the gas _____, which explains its relationship to breathing. The end products of aerobic cellular respiration are _____, _____, and _____. K/U

4. Anaerobic cellular respiration and fermentation take place in the absence of _____. The end products of fermentation can be _____ and _____. K/U

5. Label the parts of the mitochondrion in **Figure 1** below. K/U

(a) _____

(b) _____

(c) _____

(d) _____

Figure 1

MAIN IDEA: The four stages of aerobic cellular respiration are glycolysis, pyruvate oxidation, the citric acid cycle, and the electron transport chain.

6. Glycolysis starts with the molecules _____ and _____ and ends with the molecules _____, _____ and _____. It takes place in _____. K/U

7. The citric acid cycle starts with the molecules _____, _____, and _____ and ends with the molecules _____, _____, and _____. It takes place in _____. K/U

STUDY TIP

Use a Graphic Organizer
Make a comparison chart for the three main types of respiratory pathways. This will help you to understand how they are related.

8. The electron transport chain transfers high energy electrons from
   _____ and _____ to _____. The electron transfer
   results in the formation of _____, _____, _____,
   and _____. It takes place _____. K/U

9. ATP that is formed directly by the transfer of a phosphate group to ADP using
   an enzyme is referred to as _____. K/U

10. ATP that is formed indirectly by the transfer of a phosphate group through a
    series of redox reactions is called _____. K/U

MAIN IDEA: Aerobic respiration pathways use electron transport systems to generate
ATP by oxidative phosphorylation, using oxygen as the final oxidizing agent. Fermentation
pathways lack such transport systems and rely on an organic compound. Anaerobic respiration uses an inorganic substance other than oxygen as the final oxidizing agent.

11. Use **Table 1** to compare the three respiration pathways. K/U T/I

Table 1 Comparison of Respiration Pathways

	Aerobic cellular respiration	Anaerobic cellular respiration	Fermentation
Molecules used			
Location in cells			
Amount of energy produced			
Waste products			

12. Complete these paragraphs to describe the key differences between obligate
    aerobes, obligate anaerobes, and facultative anaerobes. K/U

    (a) Most eukaryotes are _____obligate_____ aerobes. This means they
        cannot live without _____O₂_____ and they use _____aerobic_____
        cellular respiration most of the time.

    (b) Organisms that can extract _____NRG_____ from food
        molecules with or without using _____O₂_____ are known as
        _____ anaerobes. _____Yeast_____ is an example of
        this type of organism.

    (c) Many organisms always extract _____NRG_____ from their food
        without using oxygen. These are called _____obligate_____ anaerobes,
        and include bacteria and protests that live in _____low-O₂_____
        environments. These organisms use two processes to extract energy:
        _____fermentation_____, which does not use an _____ETC_____ system,
        and _____anaerobic_____ respiration, which uses an _____inorganic_____
        compound as the final oxidizing agent.

Aerobic Respiration: The Details

Textbook pp. 172–182

Vocabulary

decarboxylation reaction

dehydrogenation

proton gradient

proton-motive source

chemiosmosis

MAIN IDEA: Glycolysis extracts energy from sugar molecules and produces ATP.

1. Why is the first phase of glycolysis known as the energy investment phase? K/U T/I

2. What is the source of the original two ATP molecules used in glycolysis? T/I

3. How many molecules of ATP are generated during glycolysis and how are they formed? K/U T/I

4. The fructose-1,6-biphosphate molecule appears to be symmetrical and yet it is split to form two different molecules. Identify the two molecules formed and explain how this is possible. K/U T/I

LEARNING TIP

P_i

The "P_i" used in the drawings refers to a free inorganic phosphate molecule and not to a phosphorous atom.

5. Use **Table 1** to summarize the types of chemical reactions involved during cellular respiration. K/U C

Table 1 Types of Reactions Involved in Cellular Respiration

Type of reaction	Description of reaction
phosphorylation	
isomerization	
lysis	
redox	
decarboxylation	
dehydrogenation	

6. Only 2.2 % of the energy in one glucose molecule is converted into ATP during glycolysis. The remaining 97.8 % has been lost as _____ or is still stored in _____ and _____. K/U

MAIN IDEA: Pyruvate oxidation converts two pyruvate molecules into two acetyl-CoA molecules, NADH, H$^+$, and CO$_2$ waste.

7. Fill in **Figure 1** below to show the reactants and products of pyruvate oxidation. K/U C

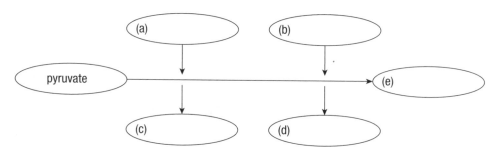

Figure 1

8. Explain why a transport protein is needed in the diffusion of pyruvate into the mitochondrion. K/U T/I

MAIN IDEA: The citric acid cycle consists of eight enzyme-catalyzed reactions. It uses acetyl-CoA to produce reducing power and energy, in the form of NADH, FADH$_2$, and ATP, and releases CO$_2$.

9. Write the names of the carbohydrate molecules involved in the citric acid cycle shown in **Figure 2**. K/U

(a) _____   (e) _____

(b) _____   (f) _____

(c) _____   (g) _____

(d) _____

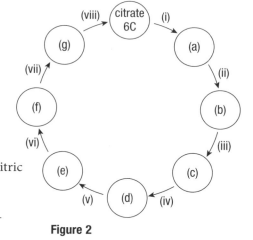

Figure 2

10. Write the names of the enzymes involved in creating each product in the citric acid cycle, shown in Figure 2. K/U

(i) _____   (v) _____

(ii) _____   (vi) _____

(iii) _____   (vii) _____

(iv) _____   (viii) _____

11. Mark the locations where carbon dioxide, NADH, and FADH$_2$ are released and where ATP is produced during the citric acid cycle on Figure 2. K/U

MAIN IDEA: The electron transport chain converts the potential energy from NADH and $FADH_2$ into chemical potential energy in ATP.

12. NADH delivers _____ p^+ _____ and _____ e^- _____ to _____ complex I _____. This causes _____ protons _____ to be pumped through the inner mitochondrial membrane. [K/U]

13. $FADH_2$ is used to deliver _____ p^+ _____ and _____ e^- _____ to _____ complex II _____ and _____ UQ _____. This causes _____ p^+ _____ to be pumped through the inner mitochondrial membrane. [K/U]

14. Where does the electron transport chain begin? Why must it begin there? [K/U] [T/I]

complex IV

15. What happens to oxygen after it draws electrons from complex IV? [K/U] [T/I]

forms water

MAIN IDEA: Chemiosmosis is the process of pumping protons across the inner mitochondrial membrane, and establishing a proton gradient. This in turn creates a proton-motive force that provides the energy used to produce ATP.

16. Describe the processes needed to move protons from the matrix into the intermembrane space. [K/U]

17. Describe the processes needed to move protons from the intermembrane space back into the matrix. [K/U]

18. Describe how the proton motive force is used to drive the production of ATP. What is the name of this type of ATP production? [K/U]

oxidative phosphorylation

MAIN IDEA: Harnessing the potential energy that is present in a proton gradient to synthesize ATP is fundamental to almost all forms of life and developed early in the evolution of life. Uncoupling electron transport and the synthesis of ATP can be caused by making the inner mitochondrial membrane permeable to protons. The energy that is released during electron transport is then converted to thermal energy.

19. Describe the purpose of brown adipose fat. [K/U] [A]

20. Suggest potential differences in brown adipose fat production for the following mammals. [K/U] [T/I] [A]

(a) large tropical mammals

(b) small temperate rodents

(c) temperate mammals that hibernate

The Efficiency and Regulation of Cellular Respiration

Textbook pp. 183–189

Vocabulary

metabolic rate   basal metabolic rate   beta-oxidation

MAIN IDEA: Aerobic cellular respiration produces a maximum of 38 ATPs per glucose molecule and has a maximum efficiency of about 41 %. Cellular respiration is regulated by negative feedback mechanisms and is able to remain flexible and responsive to changing demands for ATP. Creatine phosphate can act as a quick but short-term source of additional energy in cells.

1. Use **Table 1** to summarize the net ATP production per molecule of glucose at each stage of cellular respiration. K/U

Table 1 ATP Production During Aerobic Cellular Respiration

Stage	Number of ATP produced	Number of ATP added	Net number of ATP produced
glycolysis	10	2	8
pyruvate oxidation	6	2	4
citric acid cycle	24		24
electron transport chain			

2. Explain the role of phosphofructokinase in the control of glucose metabolism. Include a description of the conditions that inhibit and stimulate phosphofructokinase action. K/U T/I A

3. Compare the cell's use of creatine phosphate and brown adipose fat for the storage of energy. K/U T/I

MAIN IDEA: Metabolic rate and basal metabolic rate vary, based on changes in growth, development, age, health and gender. The overall rate of aerobic cellular respiration is often measured by the rate of oxygen consumption.

4. Many teenagers increase their intake of food without weight gain. Suggest examples of other uses for these excess nutrients that are not stored as fat. K/U T/I

5. The metabolic rate of an individual is difficult to measure directly. However, the rate and volume of air that an individual breathes can be directly measured. Discuss how breathing can indicate metabolic rate. K/U A

MAIN IDEA: Reactions leading from glycolysis through pyruvate oxidation are used to oxidize the glucose, other carbohydrates, lipids, and proteins that enter the cellular respiratory pathway. Many important molecules are synthesized from the intermediate chemicals produced during glycolysis and the citric acid cycle.

6. Draw a table to summarize the biochemical advantages and disadvantages of using lipids and proteins as sources of chemical potential energy during cellular respiration instead of carbohydrates. K/U T/I C

7. If a biochemist wishes to produce a weight-loss drug, how could the drug be designed to alter phosphofructokinase? K/U T/I A

MAIN IDEA: Due to the significant mass of water bonded to them, carbohydrates are heavier than lipids to carry around as fuel.

8. Suggest reasons that organisms may be adapted to use lipids and glycerol for the storage of chemical potential energy. K/U T/I

9. Suggest reasons that organisms do not use excess ATP for the storage of chemical potential energy. K/U T/I

Anaerobic Pathways: Life Without Oxygen

Textbook pp. 190–194

Vocabulary

alcoholic fermentation   lactate fermentation

MAIN IDEA: Fermentation pathways enable organisms to use glycolysis as a source of ATP, without an electron transport chain.

1. In what type of environment do organisms perform fermentation? K/U

STUDY TIP

Working Together
Working with a partner or in small groups will help you to learn and test each other on how well you understand the concepts.

2. How does fermentation affect the levels of NAD^+ and NADH? K/U

3. Name three organisms that perform fermentation. K/U

MAIN IDEA: Alcoholic fermentation is performed by yeast and has significant commercial value.

4. Use a flow chart to outline the chemical stages of alcoholic fermentation by yeast. K/U C

5. Yeast is an important commercial organism because engineers are able to use its capablilities of fermentation to create usful products. Describe two industrial uses of yeast. K/U A

MAIN IDEA: Lactate fermentation in muscles provides a supplementary source of ATP when energy demands are very high and oxygen supply is low.

6. Add labels to **Figure 1** to show the basic process of lactate fermentation. K/U C

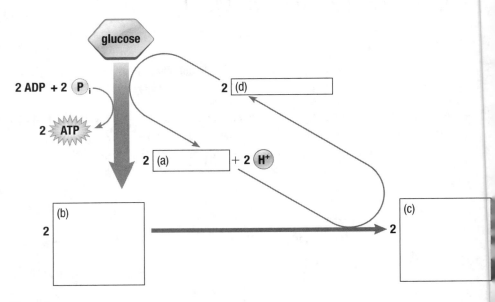

Figure 1

7. It was once thought that oxygen deficit results in the accumulation of lactic acid due to the activation of the lactic acid respiratory pathway. During strenuous exercise, lactate would accumulate in muscle tissue resulting in muscle cramps. Why is this untrue? K/U T/I

MAIN IDEA: Anaerobic respiration uses inorganic substances other than O_2 as terminal acceptors in an electron transport chain.

8. List three inorganic compounds that can be used by anaerobic organisms in place of oxygen as electron acceptors. K/U T/I

9. Use **Table 1** to compare the three types of cellular respiration. K/U C

Table 1 Cellular Respiration

	Aerobic cellular respiration	Alcoholic fermentation	Lactate fermentation
Chemicals needed			
Amount of energy produced			
Products			
Parts of cell involved			
Examples of organisms			

Biology JOURNAL

Beetroot Juice

Textbook pp. 195–196

MAIN IDEA: Beetroot juice is the latest food supplement that promises to improve athletic ability and general health. More studies are needed to prove the health benefits of beetroot juice, to explain how the supplement works, and to identify any risks.

1. What do the studies suggest is the value of beetroot juice in a diet? K/U

2. Describe one possible effect of beetroot juice on metabolism. K/U

3. Describe two experimental results that support the value of beetroot juice. K/U

4. Describe the supplement's possible chemical interactions with metabolic pathways. K/U T/I

5. Describe two effects of beetroot juice on the body as a whole. K/U T/I

Textbook pp. 197–198

Diets Programs and Supplements

MAIN IDEA: Diet programs and supplements are in demand by consumers as they strive to improve their health and quality of life. As a consumer, research is required to determine whether the diet programs or supplements are effective.

1. (a) List some of the diets that are mentioned in this section. Describe what each diet is about and how it is supposed to work. Draw a table to help organize your information. Use these headings: Diet, Description, Effect on metabolism. K/U C

LEARNING TIP

Mutliple Resources
When deciding on the risks and benefits of a proposed product, use multiple sources of information to give you a broader base of knowledge to make decisions.

(b) What do you think are some of the problems (physically and mentally) that are associated with these types of diets? T/I

Cellular Respiration

On the flow chart below, mark the locations of the formation and release of each compound listed below during cellular respiration. Be sure to include the number of each molecule used/produced at each step.

ATP

NADH

$FADH_2$

CO_2

H_2O

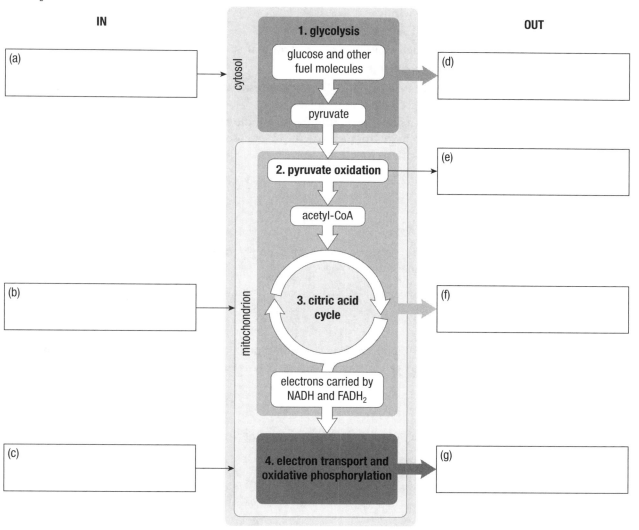

IN

OUT

(a)

(d)

cytosol

1. glycolysis

glucose and other fuel molecules

pyruvate

2. pyruvate oxidation

(e)

acetyl-CoA

(b)

mitochondrion

3. citric acid cycle

(f)

electrons carried by NADH and $FADH_2$

(c)

4. electron transport and oxidative phosphorylation

(g)

K/U Knowledge/Understanding
T/I Thinking/Investigation
C   Communication
A   Application

1. Which process converts the energy in glucose into energy in the form of ATP most efficiently? (4.4) K/U
   (a) alcohol fermentation
   (b) aerobic respiration
   (c) anaerobic respiration
   (d) lactate fermentation

2. During the process of glycolysis, some hydrogen atoms are removed from glucose in the formation of pyruvate. This is an example of which process? (4.1) K/U
   (a) hydrolysis
   (b) dehydration
   (c) dehydration synthesis (condensation)
   (d) reduction

3. Indicate whether each statement is true or false. If you think the statement is false, rewrite it to make it true. (4.1, 4.4) K/U
   (a) Cellular respiration results in the relatively rapid, uncontrolled release of energy from a molecule of glucose to produce ATP for use by cells for various functions.

   F

   (b) The electron transport chain is located on the inner portion of the cell membrane.

   F

   (c) When oxygen is scarce in human muscle tissue, lactate fermentation takes place in order to keep glycolysis running.

   T

4. Use a flow chart to summarize the major reactions of glycolysis. (4.2) K/U C

5. Distinguish between substrate level phosphorylation and oxidative phosphorylation. (4.2) K/U

6. Use a flow chart to summarize the major reactions of the citric acid cycle. (4.2) K/U C

7. Use a flow chart to summarize the major reactions of electron transport chain. (4.2) K/U C

8. Suggest three ways in which your life would be much different if humans were facultative anaerobes. (4.4) K/U T/I A

Photosynthesis: An Introduction

Textbook pp. 212–218

> **Vocabulary**
>
> photoautotroph
>
> light-dependent reactions
>
> Calvin cycle
>
> primary electron acceptor
>
> antenna complex
>
> reaction centre
>
> absorption spectrum
>
> action spectrum
>
> photosystem I
>
> photosystem II

MAIN IDEA: Producers use photosynthesis to convert light energy into chemical potential energy. Producers and consumers both use the chemical potential energy in these molecules to perform metabolism. Photosynthesis has two stages: the light-dependent reactions and the Calvin cylce.

1. (a) What is a photoautotroph?

   (b) Is a fern an example of a photoautotroph? Explain your answer. K/U T/I

2. State the main products of the light-dependent reactions. K/U

3. Suggest reasons why photosynthesis does not end immediately after the light-dependent reactions. K/U T/I

4. Why is it *not* accurate to describe the Calvin cycle as the dark reactions? K/U T/I

MAIN IDEA: The light-dependent reactions take place in the thylakoid membranes of the chloroplasts. Energy captured during the light-dependent reactions is used to synthesize NADPH and ATP.

5. Label the parts of the chloroplast, shown in **Figure 1** below. K/U

> **STUDY TIP**
>
> **Reviewing Work**
> Review the roles and interactions of ATP and NADP$^+$ in Chapter 4.

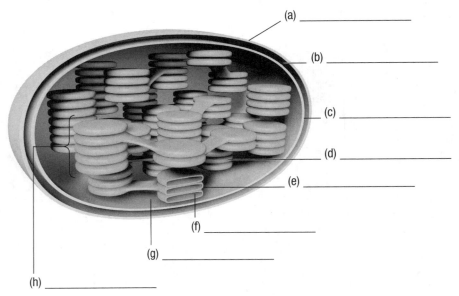

(a) _____

(b) _____

(c) _____

(d) _____

(e) _____

(f) _____

(g) _____

(h) _____

Figure 1

6. In what way does the thylakoid membrane affect the appearance of plants? K/U

MAIN IDEA: The Calvin cycle takes place in the stroma of the chloroplasts. It uses NADPH and ATP to convert carbon dioxide into simple carbohydrates.

7. Add labels to **Figure 2** to show the reactants and products of the Calvin cycle. K/U

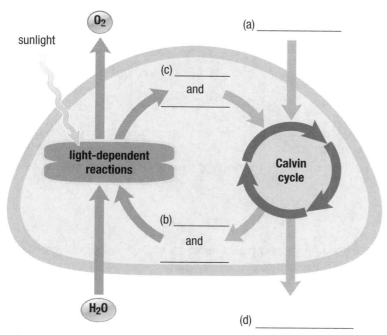

Figure 2

8. Explain the term "primary electron acceptor" in your own words. K/U C

MAIN IDEA: Chlorophylls, carotenoids, and other pigments absorb light energy during photosynthesis and are organized into two types of photosystems: photosystem I and photosystem II. Each photosystem contains a reaction centre surrounded by an antenna complex that helps capture photons. While both photosystems absorb light of slightly different frequencies, the action spectrum of both photosystems in green plants is highest in the red and blue regions of the spectrum.

9. Label **Figure 3**, which shows the pigment molecules in the antenna complex of a photosystem. K/U

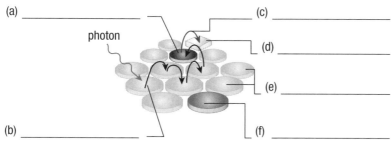

Figure 3

10. Explain differences between the structure and functions of two types of chlorophyll *a* molecules in the reaction centre. K/U

11. State an example of an accessory pigment. Describe its purpose. K/U

12. An action spectrum can be used by scientists to investigate aspects of photosynthesis. K/U T/I C
    (a) Describe the meaning of action spectrum in your own words.

    (b) How well would you expect a tomato plant to grow under a green light? Explain your prediction.

13. Draw a table to compare photosystem I and photosystem II. Use these headings: Photosystem I, Photosystem II, Type of chlorophyll, Wavelength(s) used, Products. K/U C

Pathways of Photosynthesis

Vocabulary

rubisco

Textbook pp. 220–228

MAIN IDEA: The light-dependent reactions consist of photosystem I and photosystem II. The end product of photosystem II is the powerful oxidant P680$^+$. Electrons that are excited by the light energy in photosystem II pass through the electron transport system to photosystem I. The end result of the electron transport is the production of NADPH and ATP. In cyclic electron transport, extra ATP is produced but no NADPH.

1. Label the structures in **Figure 1** to show the main compounds and reactions in photosystem II. Include arrows to show the flow of electrons and the directions and locations where hydrogen ions are pumped through the membrane. K/U C

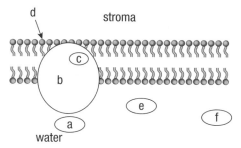

(a) _____

(b) _____

(c) _____

(d) _____

(e) _____

(f) _____

Figure 1

> **STUDY TIP**
>
> **Diagrams**
> Clear, labelled diagrams can help you study for tests. When you review your diagram, take the time to trace each step of the process it describes, locating both products and reactants.

2. Label the structures in **Figure 2** to show the main compounds and reactions in photosystem I. Include arrows to show the flow of electrons and the directions and locations where hydrogen ions are pumped through the membrane. K/U C

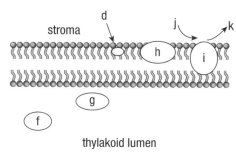

(d) _____

(f) _____

(g) _____

(h) _____

(i) _____

(j) _____

(k) _____

Figure 2

3. Describe the events that occur in the thylakoid lumen and explain the movement of protons within the thylakoid. K/U

4. Label the structures in **Figure 3** to show the main compounds and reactions in photosystem I and the synthesis of ATP. Include arrows to show the flow of electrons and the directions and locations where hydrogen ions are pumped through the membrane. K/U C

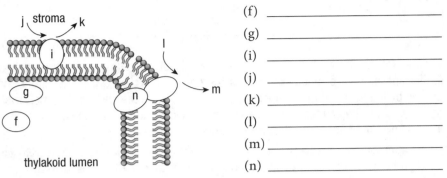

(f) _____

(g) _____

(i) _____

(j) _____

(k) _____

(l) _____

(m) _____

(n) _____

Figure 3

5. Use **Table 1** to summarize the reactions of the light-dependent stage of photosynthesis. K/U T/I

Table 1 Light-dependent Reactions

Stage	Summary
oxidation of P680	
oxidation–reduction of plastoquinone	
electron transfer of cytochrome complex and plastocyanin	
oxidation–reduction of P700	
electron transfer to NADP$^+$	
formation of NADPH	

6. During photosynthesis, the light energy is transferred to which molecules? K/U

7. Describe the function of the chlorophyll molecules, accessory pigments and proteins in a typical photosystem. K/U

8. What is the source of the electrons used in the photosynthesis reactions? K/U

9. (a) Linear electron transport results in an increased concentration of protons in what part of the chloroplast?

(b) What is this increased proton concentration used for? K/U

10. (a) Describe how ferredoxin functions with both photosystems functioning.

(b) Describe how ferredoxin functions with only photosystem I functioning. K/U

MAIN IDEA: The Calvin cycle consists of three phases: carbon fixation, reduction, and regeneration. For every three complete turns of the Calvin cycle, a single molecule of the 3-carbon molecule G3P is produced. G3P is the starting point for the synthesis of glucose, sucrose, starches, and many other organic molecules

11. Use **Table 2** to summarize the reactions that take place during each phase of the Calvin cycle. K/U

Table 2 The Calvin Cycle

Phase	Main points
carbon fixation	
reduction	
regeneration	

12. Add labels to the diagram below, which shows a single segment of the Calvin cycle that fixes only one carbon atom. Circle the areas that show carbon fixation and reduction K/U C

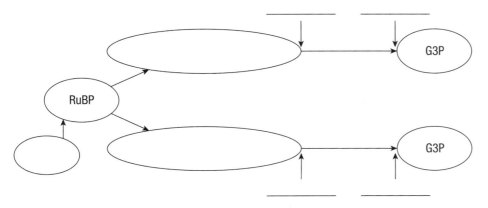

13. Glucose that is produced during photosynthesis has many uses in the plant. List four uses of glucose in the plant. K/U

5.2 Pathways of Photosynthesis **69**

Textbook pp. 229–230

The Calvin Cycle

MAIN IDEA: Melvin Calvin used a radioactive isotope of carbon (^{14}C) and two-dimensional chromatography to study the sequence of organic molecules produced during photosynthesis.

1. What were the three goals Calvin set for his experiment? Use a flow chart to link and describe the steps he took to achieve each goal. K/U C

2. (a) How is ^{14}C different than normal carbon?

   (b) Why did Calvin use ^{14}C for his experiment? Explain. K/U

3. What organism did Calvin use in his experiments? Why did he choose this organism? Explain. K/U

4. How did two-dimensional chomatography help Calvin understand what was happening during photosynthesis? T/I

Alternative Mechanisms of Carbon Fixation

Textbook pp. 231–234

Vocabulary

stomata

photorespiration

C_4 cycle

crassulacean acid metabolism (CAM)

MAIN IDEA: Many plants use the Calvin cycle (C_3 system) to fix carbon dioxide. However, some plants have evolved a C_4 pathway that all but eliminate the problem of of photorespiration associated with C_3 plants.

1. Why do plants need to fix carbon from the atmosphere? K/U

2. What is rubisco? K/U

3. Explain how the concentration of oxygen in the atmosphere affects the functioning of rubisco and can lead to photorespiration. K/U T/I

4. Add labels to **Figure** 1 below, which shows the C_4 pathways. K/U C

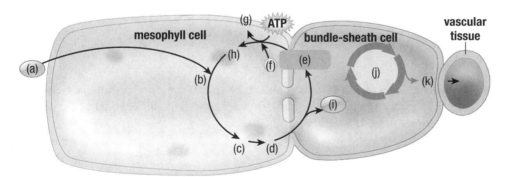

Figure 1

(a) _____   (e) _____   (i) _____

(b) _____   (f) _____   (j) _____

(c) _____   (g) _____   (k) _____

(d) _____   (h) _____

5. Using Figure 1 as a guide, make a sketch to show the differences between the arrangement of cells and the chemical pathways used in C_3 and C_4 plants. K/U C

MAIN IDEA: C_4 photosynthesis is a modification of C_3 photosynthesis, which is used to reduce photorespiration. C_4 plants are significantly more efficient than C_3 plants in performing photosynthesis in warm and/or dry environment. Many cacti and succulent plants use crassulacean acid metabolism (CAM), which uses a C_4 cycle to fix carbon during the night and the Calvin cycle to fix carbohydrates during the day.

6. Draw a table to compare C_3, C_4, and CAM plants. Compare the following features:
   - number of cells needed
   - location of of major photosynthetic cells
   - the first molecule containing fixed carbon
   - relative efficiency
   - preferred habitat of this type of plant K/U T/I C

7. A warm, dry habitat presents problems to the efficiency of carbon fixation in plants by affecting both the light-dependent and light-independent reactions. Explain why this is so. K/U T/I

Explore Applications in Artificial Photosynthesis

Can Artificial Photosystems Produce Fuel?

Textbook pp. 235–236

MAIN IDEA: Scientists from the Massachusetts Institute of Technology developed an "artificial leaf." When placed in water and exposed to sunlight, it can generate electricity. It is hoped that this device can enable homes to generate their own power.

1. Complete the graphic organizer to summarize the types of energy humans use.
   K/U C

```
          Types of Energy
         /              \
    Renewable        Non-renewable
        |                 |
   [          ]      [          ]
        |                 |
   [          ]      [          ]
        |                 |
   [          ]      [          ]
                          |
                     [          ]
```

> **STUDY TIP**
>
> **Flow Chart Displays**
> Flow charts can be written in different directions. Use the direction that is easiest for you to sort the information.

2. Complete the statements.

   Photosystem II produces _____ and _____ gas. Scientists hope to capture these products using artificial photosystems and use them to generate _____ or produce _____ to be used as a fuel.

Photosynthesis and Cellular Respiration: A Comparison

MAIN IDEA: Aerobic cellular respiration and photosynthesis create a cycle. Some of the products of one process serve as the reactants for the other process, and vice versa. Plants and most other producers perform both photosynthesis and aerobic cellular respiration. Most consumers perform aerobic cellular respiration.

1. Explain how three common chemicals on Earth circulate through the processes of photosynthesis and aerobic cellular respiration. K/U

2. Long-living plants such as trees are sometimes called carbon sinks—places where carbon is stored without increasing the amount of carbon dioxide in the atmosphere. K/U T/I

   (a) What enables plants to act as carbon sinks?

   (b) How could forest fires release the carbon?

3. Could a plant exist that performs photosynthesis but does not perform cellular respiration? Explain your answer. T/I

MAIN IDEA: The chemical processes and physical structures that are associated with photosynthesis and aerobic cellular respiration share many similarities.

4. Describe two ways in which mitochondria and chloroplasts are similar. K/U

5. Use **Table 1** to compare photosynthesis and cellular respiration. K/U

Table 1 Photosynthesis versus Cellular Respiration.

	Photosynthesis	Cellular respiration
Water		
Oxygen		
Carbon dioxide		
NAD		
Electron flow		
Proton pumps		
Uses of ATP produced		
Glucose		
Site of cyclic process		
Site of electron flow		
Site of high proton concentration		
Chemical equation		

STUDY TIP

Venn Diagrams
Venn diagrams are useful tools for comparing processes that have some similarities and some differences. After you have completed this table, think about how you would present the information in a Venn diagram.

6. Photosynthesis and cellular respiration seem to be opposite processes. On a separate sheet of paper, list some everyday processes or events that seem to be opposites. Use a graphic organizer to help you. Provide diagrams to help you explain. T/I C A

Photosynthesis: The Energy of Life

The processes that make up photosynthesis are shown as flow charts below. Add the reactants and products to complete the summary of photosynthesis.

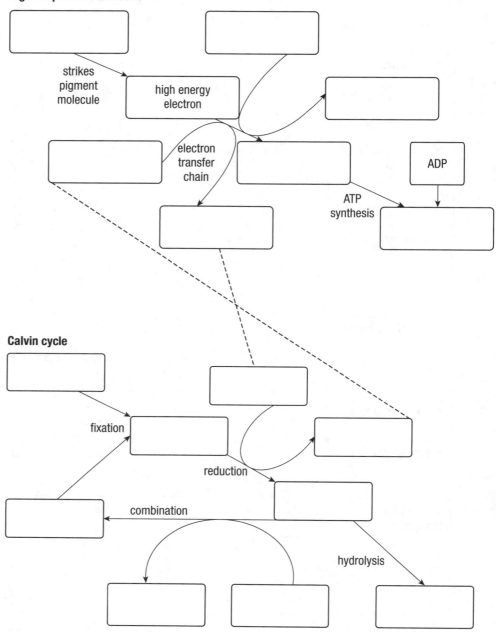

1. When photosynthetic organisms use water labelled with ^{18}O isotopes, ^{18}O is found in the oxygen produced by photosynthesis but not in the carbohydrate products. This can lead to which of the following conclusions? (5.3) K/U

   (a) The oxygen in the carbohydrate must come from carbon dioxide.
   (b) Both water and carbon dioxide are sources of gaseous oxygen.
   (c) Carbon dioxide is a possible source of oxygen gas.
   (d) ^{18}O isotopes behave differently than ^{16}O isotopes do.

2. What happens to the electrons that are released as a result of light absorption by chlorophyll? (5.2) K/U

   (a) They combine with H^+ ions and oxygen to form water.
   (b) They are used directly in the fixation of carbon during the Calvin cycle.
   (c) They reduce photosystem I chlorophyll molecules.
   (d) They reduce photosystem II chlorophyll molecules.

3. Indicate whether each statement is true or false. If you think a statement is false, rewrite it to make it true. (5.1, 5.2, 5.6) K/U

   (a) During photosynthesis light energy is transferred to ADP and $NADP^+$, forming ATP and NADPH.

   (b) Light energy is principally transferred to the primary elecron receptor by chlorophyll *b*.

   (c) In comparing respiration and photosynthesis, respiration is exergonic while photosynthesis is endergonic.

   (d) The source of electrons in photosynthesis is chlorophyll.

4. Circle the steps that are part of the Calvin cycle. (5.2) K/U

   A. ATP molecules are needed to keep the reactions going.
   B. The process makes $NADPH + H^+$.
   C. Reduction occurs.
   D. Oxygen is a product.
   E. Photophosphorylation occurs.
   F. Carbon fixation occurs.
   G. Takes place in the thylakoids of chloroplasts.

5. A type of herbicide works by disrupting the structure of the internal membranes of a chloroplast. Which process of photosynthesis is the most affected? (5.2) K/U T/I A

Sidebar legend:
K/U Knowledge/Understanding
T/I Thinking/Investigation
C Communication
A Application

6. Photophosphorylation specifically refers to the synthesis of _____
using _____. (5.2) K/U

7. Which of the following statement(s) concerning light absorption by
chlorophyll is correct? Circle your answer(s). (5.2) K/U
   A. It can take place during the fixation of carbon.
   B. It involves NADP.
   C. It occurs in the thylakoid of the chloroplast.
   D. Oxygen gas is produced.
   E. It Involves at least one carbon-containing compound.

8. Ribulose bisphosphate is converted to 3-phosphoglycerate (PGA) with the
addition of _____ and _____. (5.2) K/U

9. What is the primary cause of photorespiration? (5.4) K/U

10. How does the law of the conservation of energy and the first law of
thermodynamics apply to the light-dependent reactions of photosynthesis?
(5.2) K/U C A

11. You are touring a local greenhouse and you notice that many plants in one
room are smaller than identical plants in the other rooms. You speak with the
manager who says she has been having a problem recently with growing plants
in this particular room. Later in the conversation you learn that the manager
has looked at factors such as light levels, temperature and soil nutrients, yet
all these are the same in both rooms. What factors would you suggest testing
for? How would each of these factors affect the growth of plants? (5.1, 5.4)
K/U T/I A

1. Complete the following sentences with the appropriate vocabulary. K/U

    (a) The combustion of 10 g of glucose in oxygen gives _____ energy compared to the metabolism of 10 g of glucose by human muscle cells under aerobic conditions. (3.1)

    (b) Enzymes _____ the activation energy needed. (3.3)

    (c) The citric acid cycle occurs in the_____. (4.2)

    (d) During respiration _____ energy is transferred to _____, _____, and _____, forming _____, _____, and _____. (4.1)

    (e) Oxygen that is consumed during cellular respiration is returned to the environment once it has been combined with _____ to form _____. (4.2)

2. State whether each process below involves anaerobic or aerobic conditions. (4.1) K/U

    (a) yeast causing bread dough to rise _____

    (b) bacteria working in an aeration tank at a waste treatment plant

    _____

    (c) bacteria in the soil help in composting _____

    (d) alcohol is produced in fermentation _____

    (e) sewage breaks down in a septic tank _____

3. State whether each step or condition below is part of anaerobic respiration, aerobic respiration, or both. (4.2, 4.4) K/U

    (a) NAD^+ is reduced _____

    (b) ADP is combined with inorganic phosphate to form ATP _____

    (c) acetaldehyde is converted into ethanol _____

    (d) can release energy from glucose _____

    (e) pyruvate is formed _____

    (f) oxygen is required _____

    (g) $FADH_2$ is formed _____

    (h) takes place in the cytosol _____

    (i) is the primary method of energy production in plants and animals

    _____

4. Barbiturates are one of several classes of drugs that act by preventing the transfer of electrons through the electron transport chain of the mitochondrion. (5.2) K/U T/I A

    (a) Why are these drugs sometimes called "downers".

    (b) Why is the uncontrolled use of barbiturates dangerous?

5. Distinguish between catabolism, anabolism and metabolism. (3.1) K/U

6. Distinguish between competitive and non-competitive inhibitors. (3.3) K/U

7. Complete the following sentences to describe photosynthesis. K/U

    (a) During photosynthesis _____ energy is transferred to _____ and _____, forming _____ and _____. (5.1)

    (b) C_4 photosynthesis is a modification of C_3 photosynthesis. Its benefit to the plant is that it _____ by preventing rubisco from being exposed to oxygen. (5.4)

    (c) The CO_2 limited phase of the light response curve is a plateau, because the carbon dioxide availability, not light intensity _____ the overall rate of photosynthesis. (5.6)

    (d) The source of electrons used for photosynthesis is _____, while the source of electrons used in respiration is _____. (5.6)

    (e) In the chloroplast hydrogen ions are pumped into the interior of the _____, while in mitochondria the hydrogen ions are pumped into the _____. (5.6)

8. The chemical equation for photosynthesis is often written as shown below.

$$6\ CO_2 + 12\ H_2O \rightarrow C_6H_{12}O_6 + 6\ O_2 + 6\ H_2O$$

Why is water written on both sides of the reaction? (5.2) K/U T/I

9. Only about 5 % of the solar radiation that reaches a leaf is converted into useful stored energy. This is a low photosynthetic efficiency. (5.1) T/I A

    (a) Explain why so little energy is available to the leaf.

    (b) If you were a biological engineer, what might you do to create a more efficient plant with a higher photosynthetic efficiency?

10. You are a biochemist studying the properties of the photosynthetic enzyme, rubisco. You dissolved the enzyme in a solution that contains only carbon dioxide, magnesium ions, and an adequate supply of hydrogen ions. (5.4) K/U

    (a) What must you add to this mixture to be able to convert substrate carbon dioxide to phosphoglycerate? Explain.

    (b) Does this reaction need light to proceed? Why or why not?

11. On a separate sheet of paper, draw a Venn diagram to compare photosynthesis in chloroplasts and cellular respiration in mitochondria. Include the following terms: carbon dioxide, oxygen, water, glucose, ATP, DNA, increase in free energy, increase in potential energy, plants, animals. (5.6) C

Molecular Genetics

Chapter 6: DNA: Hereditary Molecules of Life

All living things use molecules of deoxyribonucleic acid (DNA) to carry information. DNA has a double-helix structure with a backbone of two phosphate and deoxyribose sugar strands, connected by pairs of four nitrogenous bases. The patterns in these bases make up our genes and carry all the information that allows us to function. Since the mid 1800s, when Frederick Meischer discovered the hereditary molecule he called nuclein, many teams of scientists have built on one another's discoveries to elucidate, bit by bit, the molecular structure of DNA. The current model of DNA was developed by James Watson and Francis Crick.

DNAs double-helix structure is important to its function. During replication, when the two strands of DNA separate, the complementary base pairs ensure that the two new strands that form are exact copies of the previous complementary strands.

Every time a cell divides, an exact copy of its genetic material must be passed on to each of the two daughter cells. While DNA is usually found in loose strands in the cell's nucleus, when the cell divides it bundles into tight chromosomes and is passed from generation to generation in this form. This helps ensure accurate replication. The size and number of chromosomes varies from one species to another.

Chapter 7: Genes and Protein Synthesis

The cells in an organism's body produce thousands of different proteins. Each protein is built by joining a particular sequence of amino acids. Each different sequence of amino acids produces a different polypeptide sequence. This is known as the one gene–one polypeptide hypothesis. The information needed to determine each amino acid is contained in a sequence of three nitrogenous bases in DNA, known as a codon.

The central dogma describes how the information in a gene is used to create a polypeptide. During transcription, the information in a section of DNA is encoded into messenger RNA. During translation, the information encoded in messenger RNA allows a ribosome to bind with the transfer RNA molecules carrying the correct amino acids, and insert each amino acid into the polypeptide sequence. While some polypeptides are always needed in the cell, others are only needed at certain times. The genes that code for these polypeptides are regulated by negative feedback mechanisms and by post-transcriptional regulation, such as alternative splicing.

Genetic mutations often result in a change to the protein produced. Mutations have given rise to the diversity of life, and can have positive or negative results.

Chapter 8: Genetic Technologies

Understanding the structure and the function of DNA has allowed researchers to modify existing DNA sequences. For example, a gene from one species can be inserted into a DNA vector, for example a virus, and then introduced into the genome of another species, creating recombinant DNA.

Researchers have also developed genetic technologies based on current understandings of DNA. For example, gel electrophoresis can be used to separate fragments of DNA by size, the polymerase chain reaction can be used to make many copies of short DNA sequences, and DNA microarray technology can be used to detect mutations. This has led to greatly increased abilities to study and compare sequences of DNA for scientific and forensic purposes. Genetic therapy and genetic screening are medical applications of genetic technologies.

BIG IDEAS

- DNA contains all the genetic information for any living organism.
- Proteins control a wide variety of cellular processes.
- Genetic research and biotechnology have social, legal, and ethical implications.

The Molecular Basis of Inheritance

Vocabulary

histone   genome

STUDY TIP

Using Prefixes
The prefix *eu-* means "true" so a eukaryote has a "true" nucleus.

MAIN IDEA: DNA is the molecule that carries genetic information in all living things. A gene is a region of DNA that codes for the building of a particular polypeptide.

1. Draw a flowchart to show the sequence of events that takes place when a particular protein needs to be created in a cell. K/U C

2. (a) What organelles in plants and animals contain DNA?

   (b) Which of these organelles plays a role in inheritance?

   (c) What is the term used to describe the collection of all the hereditary information in an organism? K/U

3. What is the difference between a gene and an allele? Use an example in your explanation. T/I

MAIN IDEA: Eukaryotic DNA is wound around histone proteins and organized into linear chromosomes. Chromosomes are found inside the nucleus of each cell. The genome of diploid organisms is in the form of homologous sets of chromosomes.

4. Complete the paragraph to describe the description of DNA. K/U

   DNA is passed from generation to generation in the form of
   _____. In most _____,
   chromosomes appear as the familiar _____-shaped objects that are split
   during _____ or _____. Following cell division,
   the _____ unravel to their functional form and spread
   throughout the new _____.

5. Does there appear to be a relationship between the number of chromosomes and the size or complexity of organisms? Explain. K/U T/I

6. Describe the shape and organization of DNA in eukaryotic cells. K/U

7. What function(s) does wrapping the DNA around histone proteins and coiling it into chromatin fibres serve? K/U

8. Most eukaryotic cells are diploid most of the time. Describe the meaning of diploid. K/U

9. Some eukatryotic cells are triploid or tetraploid. Sketch the chromosomes that each organism would have. C

   a diploid organism with sets of
   2 chromosomes

   (b) a triploid organism with sets of
   2 chromosomes

   (a) a diploid organism with sets of
        3 chromosomes

   (c) a tetraploid organism with sets of
        2 chromosomes

10. How many chromosomes do humans have in each body cell? K/U

MAIN IDEA: Prokaryotic cells usually have a single chromosome, which is in the form of a loop of DNA and is not associated with histones. Most of the genome is stored in this chromosome but smaller loops of DNA, called plasmids, may also be present.

11. Complete this paragraph to contrast the location of DNA in euaryotes and prokaryotes. K/U

    In _____ such as insects, birds, and mammals, DNA is
    found in paired _____ in the cell's _____.
    _____ such as bacteria and archaea, do not have a
    membrane-bound nucleus. In these organisms, most DNA is found in
    one large _____ in a region called the _____.
    Some additional DNA may also occur in smaller _____ called
    _____.

12. (a) How is the DNA of archaea similar to the DNA of bacteria?

    (b) How is the DNA of archaea similar to the DNA of eukaryotes? K/U

DNA Structure and Function: A History

Textbook pp. 273–279

> **Vocabulary**
>
> transformation   pyrimidine
>
> bacteriophage   complementary base pairing
>
> purine

MAIN IDEA: The discovery of the chemical composition, function, and structure of DNA involved the work of numerous scientists over many decades.

1. Fill in **Table 1** using the names of the scientists or teams from Chapter 6 who made major scientific discoveries during each time period. K/U C

Table 1 Major Events in DNA Research

Period	Scientist/team
1800–1900	
1900–1930	
1930–1950	
1950–1960	

2. Use **Table 2** to summarize the genetic research discussed in Chapter 6. K/U C

Table 2 A Summary of Genetic Research

Scientist/team	Summary of research
Mendel	
Meischer	
Griffith	
Avery, McLeod, and McCarty	
Hershey and Chase	
Levene	
Chargaff	
Franklin and Wilkins	
Watson and Crick	

STUDY TIP

Buidling a Body of Knowledge
Every new understanding in sience builds on preious understandings. As you read about each scientist's work, focus on how that research built on the results of earlier research.

3. New discoveries in science are often facilitated by new research technologies. Name two scientists or teams investigating DNA structure and function and describe how new research technologies helped them. K/U T/I

4. (a) New discoveries in science often build on the discoveries of others. Explain how Francis Crick and James Watson used previous discoveries about DNA to develop their model of this important molecule.

   (b) In turn, describe two discoveries about heredity and genetics that have been made possible by the work of Watson and Crick. K/U T/I

MAIN IDEA: Each nucleotide in the DNA molecule consists of a deoxyribose sugar, a phosphate group, and one of the four nitrogenous bases. The phosphates and sugars are joined together to form the backbone of each strand. The molecule is double-stranded and forms a helix. The bases are always paired together as A–T and G–C, joined by hydrogen bonds. The two strands of the molecule are antiparallel.

4. Sketch the three components of DNA. Label the three parts. K/U C

5. Complete **Table 3** to outline the major difference between purines and pyrimidines. Include the names of each of the four types of nitrogenous bases. K/U C

Table 3 A Comparison of Nitrogenous Bases

	Purines	Pyrimidines
Names		
Number of rings in structure		

6. (a) Which nitrogenous bases pair together in DNA?

(b) How many hydrogen bonds form between each pair of nitrogenous bases? K/U

7. Add labels to **Figure 1** to name the nitrogenous bases and show the locations of hydrogen bonds. K/U C

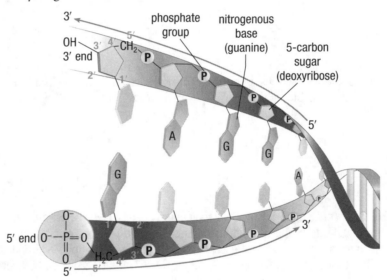

Figure 1

Biology JOURNAL

The Elucidation of the Structure of DNA

Textbook pp. 280–281

MAIN IDEA: Scientists often depend on earlier and contemporary research to reach their conclusions. Scientific research is always a balance between cooperation and competition.

1. (a) Describe the collaboration between Linus Pauling, Robert Corey, James Watson, and Francis Crick that contributed to the elucidation of the structure of DNA.

   (b) How was this collaboration helpful to both teams of scientists? K/U T/I

2. Describe Edward Chargaff's research findings about ratios of nitrogenous bases in 1950 to 1952 and how it contributed to Watson and Crick's ideas about he structure of DNA. K/U

3. Outline the research findings of Maurice Wilkins and Rosalind Franklin in 1950 to 1952. How did these influence Watson and Crick's view of Pauling and Corey's model of DNA structure? K/U

4. Why do you think it was so difficult to study and understand the structure of DNA? Give several reasons. T/I

5. Watson and Crick believed that the model they had developed could be used to develop an understanding of the mechanisms of heredity. If you were in their position, would you publish your exciting results about the structure of DNA or keep them to yourself and compete to be the first to discover the mechanism of heredity? T/I

DNA Replication and Repair

Textbook pp. 282–290

Vocabulary

semiconservative replication	replication bubble	lagging strand
replication origin	nucleoside triphosphate	Okazaki fragment
helicase	RNA primase	DNA polymerase I
replication fork	RNA primer	DNA ligase
topoisomerases	DNA polymerase III	DNA polymerase II
single-strand binding protein (SSB)	leading strand	

MAIN IDEA: DNA is copied by semiconservative replication. Each strand of the original DNA is incorporated into one of the new copies. Many steps and enzymes are involved in DNA replication. All replication begins with the formation of RNA primers on the parent DNA strands.

1. (a) Explain why DNA is described as being "replicated" instead of "copied".

   (b) Why is DNA replication referred to as semi-conservative? K/U

2. Describe the experiment Matthew Meselson and Franklin Stahl performed to study DNA replication. Be sure to describe their choice and use of radionucleotides in these studies. What was their conclusion? K/U

STUDY TIP

Using Figures with Tables
Look at Figure 3 on page 284 of your textbook. Determine the location where each enzyme or structure in Table 1 at right is active.

3. Use **Table 1** to summarize the functions of the enzymes and structures involved in strand separation, the first step of DNA replication. K/U C

Table 1 Strand Separation

Enzyme / structure	Summary of function
replication origin	
helicase	
replication fork	
topoisomerase	
single-strand binding protein	
replication bubble	

4. Use **Table 2** to summarize the functions of the enzymes and structures needed to build the complementary DNA strands, the second step of DNA replication.
K/U C

Table 2 Building Complementary Strands

Enzyme/structure	Summary of function
nucleoside triphosphate	
phosphodiester bond	
RNA primase	
RNA primer	
DNA polymerase III	
leading strand	
lagging strand	
Okazaki fragment	
DNA polymerase I	
DNA ligase	

STUDY **TIP**

Using Figures with Tables
Look at Figure 6 on page 287 of your textbook. Determine the location where each enzyme or structure in Table 2 at left is active.

MAIN IDEA: Base-pair mismatching can occur during replication. DNA polymerase and other repair mechanisms proofread the strands for errors and correct mismatched bases.

5. Use **Table 3** below to summarize the functions of the enzymes needed to check and repair errors in the complementary DNA strands, the third step in DNA replication. K/U C

Table 3 Checking and Repairing

Enzyme/occurrence	Summary of function/definition
base-pair mismatch	
DNA repair mechanism	
DNA polymerase II	

DNA Organization in Eukaryotes and Prokaryotes

Textbook pp. 291–294

Vocabulary	
nucleosome	supercoiling
solenoid	telomere

MAIN IDEA: Eukaryotic chromosomes consist of DNA bound to histones. Together, the DNA and histones form nucleosomes, which are further wound and bundled into solenoids. Bacterial DNA is circular, lacks histones, and undergoes supercoiling to reduce its volume.

1. Draw a flow chart to show how eukaryotic DNA is organized to reduce its volume. K/U C

2. (a) To what degree is eukaryotic DNA packed during interphase?

   (b) When the cell requires new proteins to be manufactured during interphase, how does it access the protein coding sequence on the DNA bases? K/U

3. Explain how prokaryotes manage to reduce the volume of their DNA. K/U

4. **Figure 1(a)** shows two bacteria cells, their chromosome, and a plasmid in one of the cells. Explain what is happening in **Figure 1(b)**. K/U C

(a)

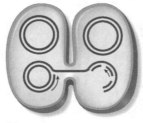

(b)

Figure 1

5. Use **Table 1** to compare prokaryotic DNA and eukaryotic DNA. K/U C

Table 1 Prokaryotic DNA versus Eukaryotic DNA

Factor	Prokaryotic	Eukaryotic
major location of DNA		
other locations of DNA		
arrangement of DNA		
histones present		
plasmids present		
nucleosome present		
solenoid present		
actual replication processes		
supercoiling present		
telomeres present		
main purpose of replication		

STUDY TIP

Comparison Questions
Comparison questions, like Question 5, are effective ways to review because you need to think about every item to place it correctly in the table, rather than just writing it down in a series of point-form notes.

6. The DNA of prokaryotes normally has only one origin of replication. In contrast, replication starts at many points on the chromosomes of eukaryotes. What would be the advantage to eukaryotes of having multiple replication sites? K/U T/I

MAIN IDEA: Telomeres are repeating sequences of DNA that are found on the ends of chromosomes. They prevent the loss of the coding regions of DNA during replication.

7. Prokaryotes do not need telomeres. Why not? K/U

8. Small pieces of the telomere are lost when the DNA replicates. Why does this not cause immediate problems? T/I

DNA Replication and Aging

Vocabulary		
cell senescence	Hayflick limit	telomerase

MAIN IDEA: Telomeres protect chromosomes from losing essential coding DNA during replication. Once a chromosome's telomeres are gone, coding DNA is lost with every replication and the cell begins a period of decline. This cellular decline is associated with many aging-related diseases. In contrast, cancer cells do not lose their telomeres, so they are functionally immortal.

1. List four important functions of telomeres. K/U

2. Why are the ends of eukaryotic chromosomes vulnerable? How do telomeres help? K/U

3. In what ways are telomeres like a biological clock? K/U

4. What is the Hayflick limit? K/U

5. Germ line cells, such as those that produce eggs and sperm, must be able to reproduce infinite numbers of times while retaining their genetic integrity. K/U T/I

    (a) Why must germ line cells be able to continue replicating without damage?

    (b) How do germ line cells avoid damage to the ends of their chromosomes?

6. (a) What lifestyle factors are associated with less shortening of telomeres in humans?

    (b) What lifestyle factors are associated with more shortening of telomeres in humans? K/U

7. Based on what you have read, do you think longer telomeres result in a longer, healthier lifespan? Explain your answer. K/U T/I

MAIN IDEA: Cancer cells have an abundance of telomerase. This enzyme keeps their telomeres from shortening and makes them functionally immortal. Medical therapies that influence the activity of telomerase and alter the length of telomeres may prove effective in the treatment and prevention of some cancers and age-related diseases.

8. How do cancer cells use their functional immortality to cause so much damage in the body? T/I

9. Some of the chemotherapy drugs used to fight cancer inhibit DNA replication. While this is sometimes successful in stopping tumour growth, there are side effects associated with this medication. What do you think one side effect might be? T/I

10. Other new therapies inhibit the production of telomerase. How do you think the effects and side effects of these therapies would compare to those that inhibit DNA replication? T/I

11. What ethical, societal, or environmental questions does research into telomere therapy raise? K/U T/I

> **STUDY TIP**
>
> **Understanding Science and Social Issues**
> All scientific research can have societal and environmental consequences. Learn to understand the science behind new findings, so that you can take part in forming the kind of world you want to live in.

DNA: Hereditary Molecules of Life

Identify the parts of the diagram to show your knowledge of DNA replication.

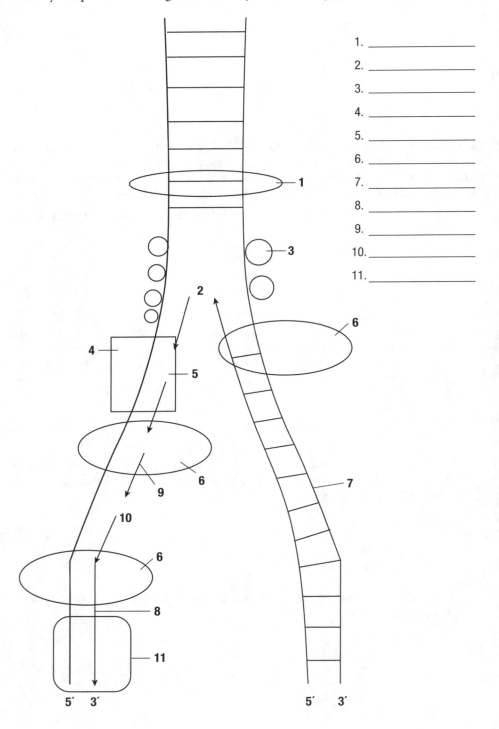

1. _____
2. _____
3. _____
4. _____
5. _____
6. _____
7. _____
8. _____
9. _____
10. _____
11. _____

1. Which statement about DNA replication is correct? (6.1) [K/U]
   (a) Prokaryotes and eukaryotes are both diploid.
   (b) It occurs before cytokinesis.
   (c) It is only semiconservative in eukaryotes not in prokaryotes.
   (d) It may be conservative or semiconservative at different points in an organism's life-cycle.

2. DNA is stable because hydrogen bonds are formed between which substances? (6.4) [K/U]
   (a) thymine and uracil
   (b) cytosine and thymine
   (c) guanine and adenine
   (d) purines and pyrimidines

3. What allows cancer cells to divide indefinitely? (6.6) [K/U]
   (a) They have no telomeres.
   (b) Their telomeres are longer than those in healthy cells.
   (c) They contain telomerase, an enzyme that regenerates telomeres.
   (d) Scientists don't know, but research is ongoing.

4. Indicate whether each statement is true or false. If you think the statement is false, rewrite it to make it true. [K/U]
   (a) DNA replication is described as semiconservative because one of the strands of the new double helix is an old strand from the parental DNA molecule, while the other has been newly synthesized using the new strand as a template. (6.4)

   (b) The five enzymes known to be responsible for DNA replication and repair in prokaryotes are DNA polymerases I, II and IV; helicase; and topoisomerase. (6.4)

   (c) The "nuclein" extracted by Meischer was acidic and rich in phosphorus and sulfur. (6.2)

5. During DNA replication, one of the new strands of DNA is synthesized continuously, while the other is synthesized as a number of separate fragments of DNA that are subsequently linked by DNA ligase. Why is this? (6.4) [K/U] [T/I]

6. The main support to the DNA molecule is provided by two backbones which run along the two sides of the double helix. Describe what these backbones consist of, and how they are formed. (6.4) [K/U]

Legend (right column):
[K/U] Knowledge/Understanding
[T/I] Thinking/Investigation
[C] Communication
[A] Application

7. How would you explain the fact that DNA that is rich in cytosine-guanine pairs requires heating to a slightly higher temperature in order to separate the strands than DNA that is rich in adenine-thymine pairs? (6.4) K/U A

8. Hydrogen bonds are quite weak compared to covalent bonds. Explain why this fact is actually advantageous to DNA in its role as the hereditary material in cells. (6.4) T/I A

9. Explain why DNA replication is slightly slower in the lagging strand of DNA than in the leading strand. (6.4) K/U

10. Imagine that you are a geneticist and you are investigating a new, unknown species of bacteriophage. How might Hershey and Chase's experiment be modified to discover whether the nucleic acid in the bacteriophage is DNA or RNA? (6.2) K/U A

11. Add labels to **Figure 1** to show the levels of organization eukaryotic DNA undergoes when tightly packed. (6.5) K/U

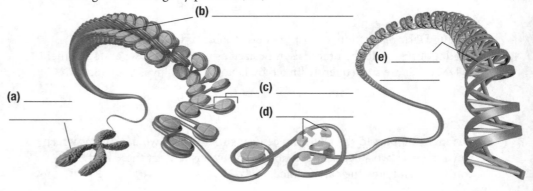

(b) _____

(e) _____

(a) _____

(c) _____

(d) _____

Figure 1

From Gene to Protein

Textbook pp. 312–318

Vocabulary

one gene–one enzyme hypothesis	translation	precursor mRNA (pre-mRNA)
one gene–one polypeptide hypothesis	messenger RNA (mRNA)	genetic code
	transfer RNA (tRNA)	codon
central dogma	ribosomal RNA (rRNA)	start codon (initiator codon)
transcription	RNA polymerase	stop codon
	template strand	

MAIN IDEA: Beadle and Tatum's experiments exposing bread mould to X-ray radiation resulted in their one gene–one enzyme hypothesis, later expanded to the one gene–one polypeptide hypothesis. A gene is a sequence of nucleotide bases that specifies the exact sequence of assembly of amino acids, by a ribosome, into a unique protein.

1. The one gene–one enzyme hypothesis had to be refined for which reason? K/U
   - (a) Some genes code for lipids and carbohydrates.
   - (b) Some genes code for many enzymes.
   - (c) Many proteins are not enzymes and are made of several protein subunits.
   - (d) Some genes are transcribed and translated into other genes.

2. Garrod's work was significant because he proposed that an individual's genetic makeup might affect that individual's ability to produce an enzyme. How did he demonstrate this? K/U
   - (a) by clarifying the nature of the disease alkaptonuria and investigating the pattern of its inheritance
   - (b) by specifying the structure of the chemical alkapton
   - (c) by investigating the structure of the enzyme which metabolizes alkapton
   - (d) by noticing that alkaptonuria was a disease normally found only in males

3. Describe the study done by Beadle and Tatum and how it relates DNA function to its structure. What were the conclusions drawn from this study? K/U

4. Describe the one gene–one polypeptide hypothesis in your own words. K/U C

MAIN IDEA: RNA differs from DNA. It is a single strand, it contains a ribose sugar instead of a deoxyribose sugar, and it contains uracil instead of thymine. Three types of RNA are involved in protein synthesis: messenger RNA (mRNA), transfer RNA (tRNA) and ribosomal RNA (rRNA). The central dogma outlines the flow of genetic information from DNA to mRNA to protein.

5. (a) Who originally proposed the central dogma?

   (b) Describe how the central dogma relates to the one gene–one polypeptide hypothesis. K/U

6. Use **Table 1** to compare DNA and RNA. K/U C

Table 1 DNA versus RNA

	DNA	RNA
Length		
Number of strands		
Location in eukaryotic cell		
Nucleotide bases		
Backbone sugar		

7. Use **Table 2** to compare the different kinds of RNA. K/U C

Table 2 Kinds of RNA

	mRNA	tRNA	rRNA
Relative length			
Location in cell			
Function			

STUDY TIP

Keep the Big Picture in Mind
You will explore the steps of the central dogma in detail in subsequent sections of this chapter. As you learn about the detailed steps, keep in mind where they fit in this overall process.

MAIN IDEA: In transcription, the information embedded in a DNA molecule is passed to a complementary mRNA molecule. In translation, the sequence of nucleotides in an mRNA molecule specifies the amino acid sequence in a polypeptide. The genetic information that specifies a single amino acid is a sequence of three bases called a codon. A single codon (AUG) signals the start of translation and three codons (UAA, UAG, UGA) signal the termination.

8. Why is RNA able to interact directly with the ribosome while DNA is not? K/U

9. How many amino acids are possible if DNA is read in groups of
   (a) three nucleotides (a three-letter code) _____
   (b) two nucleotides _____
   (c) four nucleotides _____ K/U

10. What are the similarities and differences between a start codon and a stop codon? K/U T/I

11. The convention is to write and read DNA, mRNA and tRNA from left to right. Using this convention, and Figure 7 on page 317 of your textbook, determine the amino acids that are coded for by the DNA sequence: TACAAACGT. K/U T/I

Transcription: DNA-Directed RNA Synthesis

Vocabulary

promoter	poly(A) tail	spliceosome
TATA box	5′ cap	small ribonucleoproteins (smRNP)
coding strand	exon	
termination sequence	intron	alternative splicing

MAIN IDEA: Transcription has three stages: initiation, elongation, and termination. One strand of the double-stranded DNA is used as a template for the synthesis of a single-stranded RNA molecule.

1. Use the Function column in **Table 1** to summarize the structures and events involved in transcription. K/U C

Table 1 Transcription

Event	Structure	Function
initiation	promoter and TATA box	
	RNA polymerase	
	template strand	
	coding strand	
	start codon	
elongation		
termination	stop codon	

LEARNING TIP

Coding and DNA
The coding strand does *not* code for the formation of the protein. The DNA strand that is used for coding is called the template strand.

2. Explain what is happening on each side of **Figure 1** below. K/U C

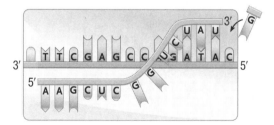

Figure 1

MAIN IDEA: In eukaryotes, post-transcriptional modifications include a 5'cap of seven Gs added to the 5' end, a string of adenines added to the 3' end, and introns excised by spliceosomes. Most eukaryotic genes contain introns (non-coding regions) and exons (coding regions). Introns are removed from a sequence by spliceosomes, the resulting sequences containing exons only are spliced together during post-transcriptional processing. There are no modifications to prokaryotic mRNA.

3. Compare and contrast the functions of adding a 5'cap and adding a poly(A) tail to mRNA. K/U T/I

LEARNING **TIP**

Introns and Exons
It helps to remember introns and exons by knowing introns are **in** the way and exons are **ex**pressed when building proteins.

4. In eukaryotes, introns are removed before mRNA leaves the nucleus. Why? K/U
   (a) The introns do not code for protein.
   (b) The introns prevent the movement of ribosomes.
   (c) The mRNA would be too long to pass through the nuclear pores if the introns remained in it.
   (d) The introns do not consist of the same bases as the rest of the mRNA.

5. Human cells have approximately 20 000 genes, but produce approximately 100 000 proteins. How can only 20 000 genes code for 100 000 proteins? K/U

6. Contrast the structure of a molecule of mRNA and the structure of the region of DNA from which it is synthesized. K/U T/I

Translation: Nucleic Acid to Polypeptide

Textbook pp. 325–331

Vocabulary

anticodon	aminoacyl-tRNA	polysome
aminoacylation	reading frame	

MAIN IDEA: tRNA molecules are small RNA molecules. Each tRNA is associated with a specific amino acid, as dictated by its respective anticodon. An anticodon is the complementary sequence to the codon associated with the specific amino acid that the tRNA carries.

1. How does the length of tRNA molecule compare to the length of an average mRNA molecule? K/U

2. Sketch a tRNA molecule. Label the anticodon, the region that carries an amino acid, and the base pairing. K/U C

3. The codons for four amino acids are listed below. Write the anticodon for each. K/U
    (a) valine (codon: GUU)   anticodon: _____
    (b) alanine (codon: GCC)   anticodon: _____
    (c) lysine (codon: AAA)   anticodon: _____
    (d) proline (codon: CCU)   anticodon: _____

4. mRNA can have 61 different codons. How can fewer than 61 different tRNA molecules be used to translate the code to synthesize the correct proteins? K/U

MAIN IDEA: Translation is the assembly of amino acids into polypeptides by a ribosome, using the information encoded in mRNA. This process has three stages: initiation, elongation, and termination. It is dependent on tRNA molecules.

5. Complete the following paragraph to summarize how a ribosome assembles a polypeptide chain. K/U

    A ribosome is made of two different parts, called the _____ and

    _____ ribosomal subunits. _____ threads through the

    ribosome. A _____ molecule, with an _____ attached to it

    and the anticodon that pairs with the _____'s codon, introduces

    the _____ to be added to the polypeptide chain next. The

    _____ is added to the chain and the _____ is released.

    Other _____ molecules add subsequent _____ to the

    polypeptide.

6. Use the Function column in **Table 1** to summarize the structures and events involved in the initiation stage of translation. K/U

Table 1 Initiation Stage of Translation

Event	Structure	Function
initiation	initiator-tRNA	
	reading frame	
	AUG	
	Methionine, short form Met	

7. Answer the following questions about the elongation stage of translation. K/U
   (a) To which site on the ribosome do all tRNAs except the first one bind?

   (b) Which site are tRNAs in when their amino acid is cleaved from them?

   (c) From which site are tRNAs released?

8. What does the ribosome do that moves a tRNA from one site to the next? K/U

9. How is a ribosome like a zipper? How do their functions differ? K/U C

10. The codons UAA, UAG, and UGA do not code for an amino acid. What are these codons known as and how do they function? K/U

Controlling Gene Expression

Textbook pp. 332–339

Vocabulary

insulin

lac operon

operator

repressor protein

inducer

corepressor

MAIN IDEA: A cell responds to changes in the environment by regulating the rate at which its genes are expressed. Prokaryotes use operons as one method to regulate gene expression. The *lac* operon is an example of enzyme induction. The *trp* operon is an example of gene repression.

1. When does the transcription of the *lacZ* and *lacY* genes of the *lac* operon begin? K/U

2. The repressor protein of the *lac* operon has two different recognition and binding sites for other molecules. Which pair of molecules would bind to these sites? K/U

   (a) RNA polymerase and lactose
   (b) the DNA sequence on the operator and lactose
   (c) the DNA sequence on the regulator gene and lactose
   (d) lactose and DNA polymerase

3. Which statement is true with respect to the *lac* operon? K/U

   (a) The repressor only binds to the operator when it is bound to the mRNA transcript of the *lacZ* and *lacY* genes.
   (b) The repressor only leaves the operator when it is bound to the protein product of the *lacI* gene.
   (c) The repressor is always bound to the operator but changes shape when lactose binds to it, allowing RNA polymerase to pass.
   (d) The repressor is bound to the operator, except when it is bound to the inducer.

4. What happens to the transcription process when there is a high cellular concentrations of tryptophan? K/U

   (a) The repressor attaches to the DNA but transcription proceeds.
   (b) Tryptophan binds to the operator and prevents transcription.
   (c) Tryptophan binds to the repressor, which than binds to the operator.
   (d) Tryptophan binds to the repressor, which binds to the promoter and prevents transcription.

5. Label **Figure 1** to show the effect of lactose on the *lac* operon complex. K/U C

> **LEARNING TIP**
>
> ***Lac* Operon Regulation**
> Regulation of the *lac* operon is a negative feedback loop. You will learn about other negative feedback loops in Chapter 9: Homeostasis.

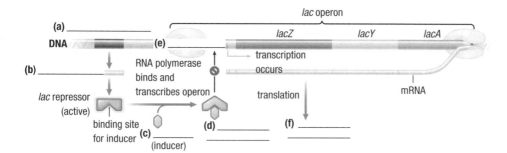

Figure 1

MAIN IDEA: Gene regulation in eukaryotes can occur during transcription, post-transcription, translation, or post-translation.

6. Describe what is happening at stage 1 and 2 in **Figure 2**. K/U T/I C

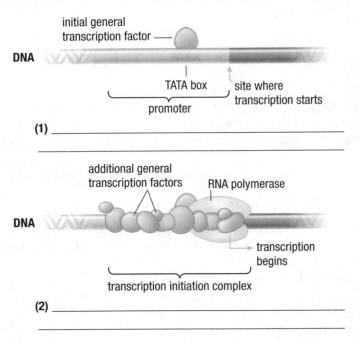

(1) _____

_____

(2) _____

_____

Figure 2

7. Use **Table 1** to summarize the gene regulation methods used by eukaryotes. K/U C

Table 1 Eukaryotic Gene Regulation

Gene regulation methods	Summary
transcription	
post-transcription	
translation	
post-translation	

8. How does gene expression control the growth of cancerous cells? Why do most cancers occur more often in old age? Explain. K/U T/I

Genetic Mutations

Vocabulary

point mutation

substitution

insertion

deletion

inversion

single nucleotide
 polymorphism (SNP)

missense mutation

nonsense mutation

silent mutation

frameshift mutation

translocation

spontaneous mutation

induced mutation

mutagen

Textbook pp. 340–345

MAIN IDEA: A mutation is a change in the sequence of DNA. A point mutation is specific to one base pair. Substitution involves the replacement of one base pair with another base pair. Small-scale mutations such as these can be classified as silent mutations, missense mutations, nonsense mutations, or frame shift mutations. Large-scale mutations include translocations, and inversions.

1. Use **Table 1** to summarize the types of small-scale mutations and their effects. K/U C

Table 1 Types of Small-scale Mutations

Mutation	Resultant change to the DNA sequence	Effect of change
point mutation		
substitution		
insertion		
deletion		
single nucleotide polymorphism (SNP)		

2. Compare and contrast translocations and inversions. K/U T/I

> **STUDY TIP**
>
> **Simple Diagrams**
> This section includes definitions of many types of mutations. Draw a simple diagram of each one to help you remember how it affects the genome.

3. Use **Table 2** to summarize the four groups of mutations and their effects. Then rank each group from 1 to 4, where 1 usually results in the least amount of change and 4 usually results in the most amount of change. K/U T/I C

Table 2 Mutations and Their Effects

Mutation	Description	Effect of change and rank
missense mutation		
nonsense mutation		
silent mutation		
frameshift mutation		

MAIN IDEA: Mutations can either arise spontaneously or be induced by mutagens. Mutagens include radiation and certain chemicals.

4. What causes spontaneous mutations? K/U

5. List several examples of mutagens that typically result in induced mutations. K/U

6. Compare and contrast the impact of mutations on the individual and on the population. K/U T/I

7. Are genetic mutations good or bad? Justify your opinion. T/I C

Genomes and Gene Organization

Textbook pp. 346–349

Vocabulary

Human Genome Project

variable number tandem
   repeats (VNTRs)

LINEs (long interspersed
   nuclear elements)

SINEs (short interspersed
   nuclear elements)

transposon

pseudogene

comparative genomics

MAIN IDEA: Genome organization refers to the sequential structure of a genome. The human genome is composed of coding and non-coding regions. Only 2 % of the genome codes for proteins. The remaining genome is composed of introns within genes and repeating sequences between genes. The eukaryotic genome also contains transposons and pseudogenes.

1. Label the parts of the chromosome segment in **Figure 1**. K/U C

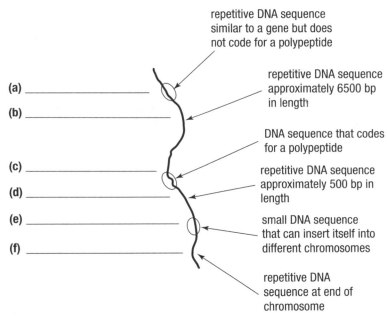

(a) _____

(b) _____

(c) _____

(d) _____

(e) _____

(f) _____

repetitive DNA sequence
similar to a gene but does
not code for a polypeptide

repetitive DNA sequence
approximately 6500 bp
in length

DNA sequence that codes
for a polypeptide

repetitive DNA sequence
approximately 500 bp in
length

small DNA sequence
that can insert itself into
different chromosomes

repetitive DNA
sequence at end of
chromosome

Figure 1

2. Sketch a circle graph to show the proportion of the human genome that is made up of each of the following: protein-coding sequences, introns, functional DNA such as regulatory sequences, and repeated sequences of non-functional DNA. K/U C

STUDY TIP

Graphic Organizers
Graphs and tables are effective ways to show a lot of information in a small amount of space. If you include them in your notes, you will find it easier to review the main points.

3. How can pseudogenes help scientists map evolutionary relationships between species? K/U T/I

4. Is a species with a larger genome more complex than a species with a smaller genome? Explain. K/U

MAIN IDEA: The declining cost and increasing efficiency of genomic technologies raises numerous ethical questions about the use of genomic information.

5. In 2006, the National Geographic Society offered members a chance to have their own genome read for a fee. The main purpose of this offer was to collect DNA samples for research on the Y chromosome and human migration patterns. K/U T/I A

(a) Should any copies of an individual's genome be stored by the National Geographic Society or the research team? Why or why not?

(b) What is the value, if any, of having your own genome sequenced?

(c) Suppose you requested to have your genome sequenced and analyzed. and you were told that the gene that codes for the enzyme telomerase is different than normal. Does this mean you will lose your telomeres at an early age, and your cells will stop dividing? Would you want to know this information?

Viruses: A Special Case

Textbook pp. 350–353

Vocabulary		
reverse transcriptase	retrovirus	transduction

MAIN IDEA: Viruses have small genomes that consist of only RNA or DNA. They rely on their hosts genetic machinery to replicate themselves. Many errors are made by a virus's polymerase enzymes and, as a result, there is a very high mutation rate.

1. What characteristic of viruses may lead you to believe they are living? K/U

2. What characteristics of viruses may lead you to believe they are not living? K/U

3. Is the high mutation rate in viruses an advantage or a disadvantage? Explain. T/I A

MAIN IDEA: A retrovirus uses an enzyme called reverse transcriptase to synthesize complementary DNA from an RNA template. This allows new virus particles to be assembled.

4. Complete this description of the steps in the life cycle of a retrovirus. K/U

   A retrovirus injects _____ and the two enzymes _____, and _____ into a host cell. Using _____ from the host cell and _____, two strands of complementary viral _____ are synthesized from the viral _____. The enzyme _____ incorporates these into the host cell's _____. There, they produce more viral _____, which exits the host cell and serves as the genome for new _____.

5. What advantages does the use of a host cell and reverse transcriptase give to a retrovirus? K/U T/I

> **STUDY TIP**
>
> **Diagrammatic Flow Charts**
> A diagrammatic flow chart, like Figure 3 on page 352 of your textbook, can help you keep track of the steps of this process.

6. (a) Label the two structures that surround the virus in **Figure 1**.

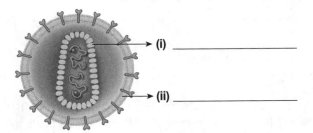

(i) _____

(ii) _____

Figure 1

(b) Could the virus shown in Figure 1 be a retrovirus? Explain. K/U C A

MAIN IDEA: Viruses have many research and therapeutic applications because of their unique genetic properties. One example is the use of viral vectors to introduce new genetic material into an existing cell in a process called transduction.

7. (a) What evolutionary advantage would the ability to use transduction convey to viruses?

(b) What evolutionary effects could viral transduction have on other species? T/I A

8. Discuss how research using viral transduction can be used to benefit humans, its possible benefits and its possible drawbacks. K/U C

Genes and Protein Synthesis

Label **Figure 1** and **Figure 2** to review what you have learned about transcription and translation.

Transcription

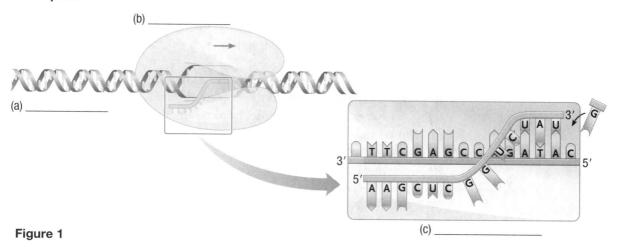

Figure 1

Translation

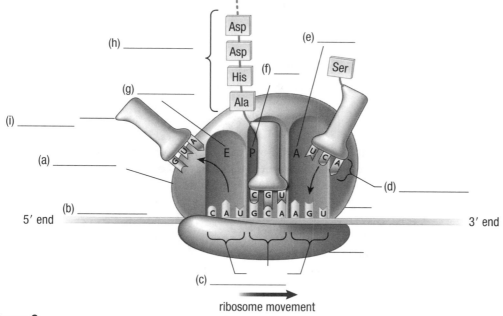

ribosome movement

Figure 2

K/U Knowledge/Understanding
T/I Thinking/Investigation
C Communication
A Application

1. Which list correctly shows the order in which the cellular machinery becomes involved in protein synthesis? (7.3) K/U
   (a) DNA polymerase, mRNA, ribosome, tRNA
   (b) mRNA, RNA polymerase, ribosome, tRNA
   (c) RNA polymerase, mRNA, tRNA, ribosome
   (d) RNA polymerase, mRNA, ribosome, tRNA

2. Segment A of DNA is rich in adenine. Segment B is rich in cytosine. The two segments are the same length. Which statement about the two segments is true? (7.1) K/U
   (a) Segment A will require more energy to unwind.
   (b) Segment B will require more energy to unwind.
   (c) The two segments will require the same amount of energy to unwind.
   (d) Not enough information is given to decide which segment will require more energy to unwind.

3. RNA polymerase functions in which process? (7.2) K/U
   (a) DNA transcription
   (b) DNA replication
   (c) RNA transcription
   (d) RNA translation

4. Indicate whether each statement is true or false. If you think a statement is false, rewrite it to make it true. K/U
   (a) The anticodon for the mRNA codon CGA is GCT. (7.3)

   (b) The structure of ethidium bromide is responsible for its ability to mutate DNA and is an example of a chemical mutagen. (7.5)

   (c) The mRNA transcript of a gene is made up of the complementary neucleotide bases to the template strand of DNA except that the uracil in DNA will be replaced by the thymine. (7.2)

   (d) The fact that the genetic code is very different in almost all organisms indicates that it evolved early in the history of life on earth. (7.6)

5. A cell in culture is briefly immersed in radioactive uracil. After a short time, the radioactive uracil is removed and the cell culture is washed with, and immersed in, non-radioactive uracil. Where would you expect to find the main concentration of radioactive nucleic acid for each time period? (7.2, 7.3) K/U A
   (a) immediately after immersion in the radioactive uracil solution

   (b) some time after the cell was returned to nonradioactive uracil

6. There are differences in the amino acid sequence of rabbit and frog hemoglobin polypeptides. If mRNA for rabbit hemoglobin is extracted from rabbit red blood cells, and is then placed in frog eggs, the cells will produce rabbit hemoglobin polypeptides. What does this demonstrate? (7.6) K/U T/I

7. Compare the two mRNA sequences below.
AUAUUCGGCAAUCCG
AUAUUCCGCAAUCCG
This change could be the result of a which type of mutation? Explain. (7.5) K/U A

8. The operator of the *lac* operon is upstream of the genes, which code for enzymes. What does upstream mean in this context? (7.4) K/U

9. What is the function of the polyadenine tail that is added to mRNA in eukaryotic cells? (7.2) K/U

10. Briefly explain how DNA is capable of encoding a great deal of information in spite of its apparently simple structure. (7.1) K/U C

11. Use **Table 1** to compare transcription and translation. (7.2, 7.3) K/U T/I

Table 1 Transcription versus Translation

	Transcription	Translation
Initiation		
Elongation		
Termination		

12. Some people suggest that the study of human diseases could be made easier if cloned transgenic animals were produced that carried faulty versions of human genes, such as the gene that causes cystic fibrosis. (7.7) T/I
    (a) Why would such animals be useful in medical research?

    (b) What ethical questions are raised by the creation of such transgenic animals?

Manipulating and Cloning DNA

Textbook pp. 366–375

Vocabulary

diabetes mellitus	recognition site	copy number
type 1 diabetes	restriction fragment	host cell
type 2 diabetes	blunt end	cloned gene
genetic engineering	sticky end	restriction map
recombinant DNA	competent cell	hybridization probe
restriction enzyme	vector	

STUDY **TIP**

Prokaryotic DNA
Review prokaryotic DNA organization and conjugation in Section 6.5 of your textbook, on page 292.

MAIN IDEA: Appropriate restriction enzymes are used to excise a relatively small DNA fragment containing the target gene from the original DNA.

1. Describe the relationship between the terms "genetic engineering" and "recombinant DNA." K/U T/I

2. Explain how restriction enzymes function. Include the following terms in your explanation: recognition site; palindrome; restriction fragment; sticky end; blunt end. K/U C

3. **Table 1** lists some examples of restriction enzymes. Use Table 1 to show how each pair of DNA sequences below will be cut. Include the name of each restriction enzyme used and the type of end produced. K/U T/I

Table 1 Examples of Restriction Enzymes

Enzyme name	Recognition site	Restriction fragments	
XhoI	5'-CTCGAG-3' 3'-GAGCTC-5'	5'-C 3'-GAGCT	TCGAG-3' C-5'
Hind III	5'-AAGCTT-3' 3'-TTCGAA-5'	5'-A 3'-TTCGA	AGCTT-3' A-5'
SmaI	5'-ACCCGGGT-3' 3'-TGGGCCCA-5'	5'-ACCC 3'-TGGG	GGGT-3' CCCA-5'
AluI	5'-AGCT-3' 3'-TCGA-5'	5'-AG 3'-TC	CT-3' GA-5'
SaII	5'-GTCGAC-3' 3'-CAGCTG-5'	5'-G 3'-CAGCT	TCGAC-3' G-5'

a) 5' - CCACTCGAGCGTTACGTCGACGGGCATTTCCAGCT - 3'
    3' - GGTGAGCTCGCAATGCAGCTGCCCGTAAAGGTCGA - 5'

b) 5' - AGGAAGCTTAACACTTGTTACCCGGGTACGCAACTTAGC - 3'
    3' - TCCTTCGAATTGTGAACAATGGGCCCATGCGTTGAATCG - 5'

4. Describe the normal use of the enzyme ligase by cells and how this enzyme is used in biotechnology. K/U

MAIN IDEA: To construct a recombinant DNA molecule, the target gene is ligated to a DNA vector. Plasmids are one example of a vector. Bacterial host cells can be manipulated to take up foreign DNA using a calcium chloride transformation solution. In most cases, cells that have been successfully transformed with recombinant DNA are isolated based on their ability to resist an antibiotic. Those that contain plasmids with the target gene are identified using hybridization techniques.

5. Describe the normal use of plasmids by bacteria and how plasmids are used in biotechnology. K/U

6. Explain how a biotechnologist might make use of a plasmid restriction map. K/U A

7. Construct a plasmid restriction map for plasmid X using the data in **Table 2**. K/U T/I C

Table 2 Results of a Restriction Enzyme Digestion of Plasmid X

Plasmid X uncut	Plasmid X cut with EcoRI	Plasmid X cut with BamHI	Plasmid X cut with EcoRI and BamHI
2100 bp	2100 bp	900 bp 1200 bp	150 bp 900 bp 1050 bp

8. Describe the normal use of transformation by bacteria and how transformation is used in biotechnology. K/U A

DNA Sequencing: PCR and Gel Electrophoresis

Textbook pp. 376–385

Vocabulary

polymerase chain reaction (PCR)	molecular marker	whole-genome shotgun method	bioinformatics
	ethidium bromide		DNA microarray
DNA primer	DNA sequencing	structural genomics	
gel electrophoresis		functional genomics	

MAIN IDEA: The polymerase chain reaction (PCR) is used to rapidly make many copies of short DNA sequences. This is useful for applications in which only a tiny sample is available, such as forensic applications.

1. Use **Table 1** to summarize the steps used in the PCR process. K/U C

Table 1 The PCR Process

Step	Summary of Function
denaturation	
annealing	
extension	

STUDY **TIP**

Venn Diagrams
Using a Venn diagram is a very effective way to analyze similarities and differences between two related concepts or processes.

2. Use the Venn diagram below to compare PCR and DNA replication. K/U C

PCR   DNA Replication

MAIN IDEA: DNA fragments are separated by size using gel electrophoresis.

3. Describe the process of gel electrophoresis. Include an explanation of why the DNA fragments move and why they move at different rates. K/U T/I

4. How are DNA fragments visualized after gel electrophoresis? K/U

MAIN IDEA: Genomes are analyzed structurally to determine the DNA sequence. DNA sequencing can be done using the Sanger method (chain termination method) and the shotgun method. Genomes are analyzed to understand the function of each gene, the protein it codes for, and the function of the protein in the cell.

5. Describe how Frederick Sanger determined the sequence of DNA. K/U

6. Describe how Craig Venter determined the sequence of DNA. K/U

7. What is the purpose of knowing the sequence of DNA nucleotides in an organism's genome? Explain from both the structural and functional perspectives. K/U T/I C A

MAIN IDEA: Nanopore sequencing is a promising method that could be cheap, quick, and easy. It involves running a DNA strand through a tiny hole and measuring the current. DNA microarray technology can be used to detect mutations, study gene functions, and compare the expressions of genes in different tissues, individuals, and organisms.

8. Suggest one way in which nanopore sequencing could help scientists study genetic mutations. T/I A

9. Explain the purpose of DNA microarray in understanding the functions of specific genes within a certain cell type or organism. K/U T/I

Genetic Engineering: Redesigning Life

> **Vocabulary**
>
> biopharming   transgenic organism (genetically modified organism, GMO)

MAIN IDEA: Genetic engineering produces transgenic, or genetically modified, organisms by inserting DNA from one species into another species. GMOs can offer a lot of benefits for humans, such as higher crop yields and lower dependence on herbicides and pesticides.

1. Complete the description of genetic engineering. K/U

   Genetic engineering uses _____ technology to modify the _____ of a cell or an organism. In this way, new _____ can be introduced into an organism, such as the ability to produce new _____. These _____ can be removed and used in manufacturing, for example the manufacturing of pharmaceutical products. This process is known as _____. An organism that has been changed by scientists to contain one or more _____ from another _____ is known as a _____ or_____ organism. If the genetic change is engineered in the _____ of the species, it is passed on to the offspring.

2. Suggest a reason why each organism in **Table 1** might be more beneficial to humans if it were genetically modified. K/U T/I C A

   Table 1 Benefits of Genetically Modified Organisms

Organism	Possible benefits
bacteria	
yeast	
tomatoes	
rice	
canola	
soybeans	
cotton	
cattle	
salmon	
goats	

MAIN IDEA: Plants and animals are often used in genetic engineering rather than bacteria, because they are more economical to maintain and they can produce larger molecules. Because genetic engineering is a new biotechnology, many people are concerned that there may be far-reaching, irreversible harmful effects.

3. (a) What are knockout mice?

   (b) What is their value to scientists? K/U

4. (a) Describe four risks of using transgenic plants and animals.

   (b) Which of the risks you described in part (a) have been shown to be real? Explain. K/U T/I

STUDY **TIP**

Technology Analysis
New technologies often come with both benefits and drawbacks. It is important to be able to analyze the significance of each and come to your own conclusion about the technology's usefulness and merit.

5. Classify the political and economic concerns about using transgenic plants and animals by completing the Venn diagram. K/U T/I C

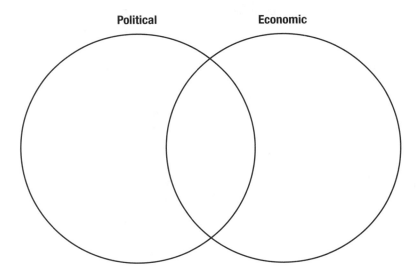

Political   Economic

6. The benefits and concerns related to genetic engineering are very diverse and interest people in many fields. List ten occupations that may be interested in the applications and risks of genetic engineering. T/I

Biotechnology and Health

Textbook pp. 391–394

> **Vocabulary**
>
> gene therapy   somatic gene therapy   amniocentesis
>
> germ-line gene therapy   genetic screening

MAIN IDEA: Genetic therapy involves replacing, removing, inserting, or repairing defective genes with ones that function properly.

1. Complete the following description of two types of genetic therapy. K/U

   Somatic gene therapy improves the functioning of an individual's

   _____ cells but the _____ are not passed on to any

   _____. Germ-line gene therapy involves changes to _____

   cells and _____ so changes in an individual's DNA are passed on to

   the _____.

2. Describe several ways that a person with a genetic disorder could be helped by genetic therapy. K/U A

3. Use the Venn diagram below to compare germ-line gene therapy and somatic gene therapy. K/U C

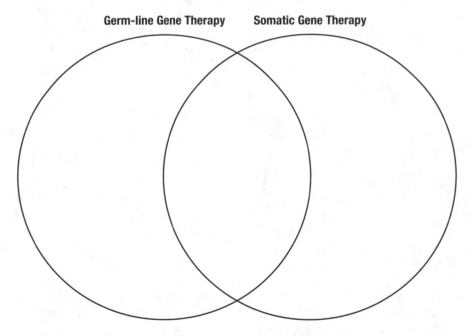

Germ-line Gene Therapy   Somatic Gene Therapy

4. Why is germ-line gene therapy not practised on humans? T/I

5. (a) Describe the first successful use of gene therapy with a human subject.

(b) How did this the therapy you described in part (a) change the subject's life? K/U T/I

6. Despite successes, human gene therapy is still in experimental stages. Why has it not yet been approved for commercial use? T/I

MAIN IDEA: Genetic screening consists of biochemical or molecular tests to identify inherited disorders in people.

7. How is genetic screening different from genetic therapy? K/U

8. (a) Describe two conditions that can be detected with genetic screening.

(b) For each condition you described in part (a), describe how genetic screening can help people manage the condition. K/U T/I

Biology JOURNAL

Textbook pp. 395–396

Sequencing the Human Genome: The Role of Collaboration and Competition in Science

MAIN IDEA: Competition between two groups of scientists attempting to map the human genome accelerated the projects so that both teams finished ahead of schedule. The completion of the project has had many benefits.

LEARNING TIP

The Genome Project
The spirit of competition and collaboration that led to the sequencing of the human genome are common to many scientific investigations. Watch for how they act to further scientific research in other areas.

1. The race to complete the human genome project highlighted a secondary debate about how scientific research should be funded and used. The scientific community (the public team of Francis Collin) felt that the entire population should pay using money collected through taxation. The results would then be freely available to anyone who wished to use them. The business community (the private team of Craig Venter) felt that companies could fund the projects privately and anyone who wanted to use the results could purchase them like any other product. What is your view on how to fund this research and who should own the results? K/U T/I C A

2. Former U.S. President Bill Clinton compared the Human Genome Project to a map. In what ways are they similar? In what ways are they different? K/U T/I

3. The Human Genome Project used the DNA samples of less than one hundred people. Do you think the data they gathered is truly representative of the human race? Explain. K/U T/I A

Should DNA Samples Be Collected from Everyone?

Textbook pp. 397–398

MAIN IDEA: The ability to store and analyze DNA samples raises many ethical issues.

1. It is important for a society to balance the rights of individuals with the rights of all the other stakeholders. For example, individuals in Canada have the right to freedom of speech, but they do not have the right to promote hatred against others. Based on what you know about DNA analysis and on your research, complete **Table 1** to describe arguments for and against the use of DNA forensics. T/I C

LEARNING TIP

The Nature of Science
Science is not an isolated discipline. It has many connections with other aspects of our lives. Be alert for them as you analyze this issue and other scientific issues.

Table 1 Balancing Rights Related to DNA Forensics

For use of DNA forensics	Against use of DNA forensics

2. Do you think that a police registry of DNA could be kept confidential and not shared with other organizations? Explain. K/U T/I A

Genetic Technologies

Fill in the flow chart below to show the process of finding a gene that codes for a desired protein and making it into a commercial product or therapy.

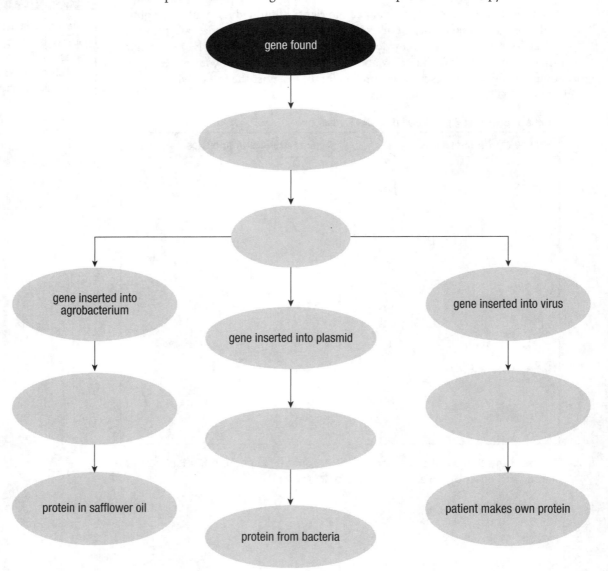

gene found

gene inserted into agrobacterium

gene inserted into plasmid

gene inserted into virus

protein in safflower oil

protein from bacteria

patient makes own protein

1. Why was the discovery of restriction endonucleases crucial to the development of recombinant DNA technology? (8.1) K/U
   (a) The enzymes always cut DNA at either end of a gene.
   (b) The enzymes cut DNA at specific and predictable sequences of bases.
   (c) The enzymes tag DNA so that individual fragments can be identified.
   (d) The enzymes all cut DNA, leaving sticky ends.

2. When recombinant DNA is formed, it is necessary to join the sugar-phosphate backbones of the plasmid DNA and the introduced DNA. Which tool is used to do this? (8.1) K/U
   (a) thermal energy
   (b) DNA polymerase
   (c) DNA helicase
   (d) DNA ligase

3. Why are dideoxinucleotides used in the Sanger process of DNA sequencing? (8.2) K/U
   (a) They stop the synthesis of elongating DNA strands.
   (b) They are fluorescent.
   (c) They move quickly during gel electrophoresis.
   (d) They stabilize small double-stranded DNA fragments.

4. Indicate whether each statement is true or false. If you think a statement is false, rewrite it to make it true. K/U
   (a) During the polymerase chain reaction, RNA primers are used that are complementary to part of the DNA to be copied. (8.2)

   (b) Some restriction endonucleases make zigzag cuts in double-stranded DNA, leaving blunt ends. (8.1)

   (c) During gel electrophoresis, DNA fragments migrate through the gel at a rate that is inversely proportional to the logarithm of their size. (8.2)

   (d) The use of Taq polymerase has made PCR faster and cheaper. (8.2)

   (e) It is important to select a restriction nutrient that does not cut in the plasmid's origin of replication, otherwise the plasmid will fail to replicate properly. (8.1)

   (f) If only a small or degraded sample of DNA is available, PCR analysis is used because it has the capacity to amplify the genetic material available. (8.2)

5. What type of bonds can restriction endonucleases break? (8.1) K/U

K/U Knowledge/Understanding
T/I Thinking/Investigation
C   Communication
A   Application

6. You are a geneticist who is interested in a particular gene on human chromosome number eight. You have used a restriction endonuclease to produce fragments of the chromosome and cloned each fragment in a different culture of bacteria. You now need to find out which culture contains the fragment with the gene of interest. You have available to you a single-stranded radioactive DNA probe complementary to the template strand of the gene. In what order would you perform the following steps for each of the bacterial colonies? (8.2) K/U

_____ Allow annealing between the probe and the DNA from the bacteria to occur.

_____ Flood the culture with the DNA probe.

_____ Separate the strands of double-stranded DNA from the bacteria using heat.

_____ Break open the bacteria.

_____ Prepare an autoradiograph.

_____ Wash away unannealed probes.

7. How are fragments of DNA separated during gel electrophoresis? (8.2) K/U

8. The human gene that codes for insulin can be inserted into an *E. coli* plasimd. The *E. coli* will then produce insulin. Is the altered *E. coli* plasmid recombinant DNA? Why or why not? (8.1) K/U A

9. When gel electrophoresis is undertaken, one lane always contains DNA-marker molecules. What are these markers and what is their purpose? (8.2) K/U

10. Genetic screening makes it possible to identify genetic disorders that might affect a person later in life. In Canada, most health care costs are paid for by the government. Some people would like to shift more of the cost of health care to individuals. How do you think doing this might affect the number of people who undergo genetic screening? (8.4) T/I C

11. Some people suggest that there is really no difference between using genetic engineering and using traditional selective breeding methods or hybridization to produce new plant and animal varieties. Do you agree? Explain. (8.3) K/U T/I C A

1. The model for DNA structure proposed by Watson and Crick, by its very nature, suggests a way in which the DNA molecule can replicate itself. Why is this? (6.2) K/U
   (a) Each base is capable of specifying the base opposite to it in the double helix.
   (b) The two strands are held together by hydrogen bonds.
   (c) Only four different bases are involved in the structure.
   (d) Hydrogen bonds only form when the strands are anti-parallel.

2. Restriction endonucleases existed before genetic engineering. What function did these enzymes originally serve? (8.1) K/U
   (a) They destroy bacterial DNA.
   (b) They are a part of the immune system of animals.
   (c) They destroy bacteriophage DNA.
   (d) They are components of spliceosomes.

3. Indicate whether each statement is true or false. If you think a statement is false, rewrite it to make it true. K/U
   (a) The central dogma states that the flow of genetic information is in the following direction: protein, RNA, DNA. (7.1)

   (b) Mutations can be inheritable if they affect somatic cells. (7.5)

   (c) The genetic change responsible for sickle cell anemia is a point mutation. (7.5)

4. Evolution is driven by changes in DNA and proteins. Normally, the rate of evolution appears slow and the evolution of a given species impacts the evolution of other species in the community. Suggest how the introduction of foreign DNA into widespread species, such as canola, soybeans or wheat, might affect evolution over whole ecosystems. (8.3) T/I A

5. Antibiotics and vaccines have proven to be powerful tools in combating pathogenic diseases. It is hoped that biotechnology will do the same for cancers and genetic disorders. Use a T-chart to compare the application and effectiveness of these methods of controlling disease. (8.4) K/U T/I C A

K/U Knowledge/Understanding
T/I Thinking/Investigation
C Communication
A Application

6. Use **Table 1** to summarize the differences between DNA replication in eukaryotes and prokaryotes. (6.2, 6.4, 7.2) K/U C

Table 1 Prokaryotes versus Eukaryotes

	Prokaryotes	Eukaryotes
Location of DNA		
DNA organization		
Chromosome organization		
Replication origin		
Telomeres present?		
Exchange of DNA between individuals		
Types of RNA polymerase used		
Speed of transcription		
mRNA termination		
Introns present?		
Speed of translation		
Initiation at ribosome		
Control of gene expression		
Acceptance of foreign DNA		
Ability to build foreign protein		

7. Use the DNA sequences below to answer the following questions. Refer to Table 1 on page 367 of your textbook for examples of restriction enzymes. Refer to Figure 7 on page 317 of your textbook for the codons in mRNA. (7.1, 7.2, 8.1, 8.2) T/I A

   (a) Determine the amino acid sequence of the normal DNA sequence.
   (b) Circle the DNA mutations.
   (c) Name the type of mutation seen in mutations 1 and 2.

   (d) Determine the amino acid sequences for mutations 1 and 2. Highlight the changed amino acids, if any.
   (e) Which mutation could be seen using gel electrophoresis? Why?

   Normal:
   5' TAC GGT CCC AGC TTA AAG CTT ATC CGG GT 3'

   Mutation 1:
   5' TAC GGA TCC CAG CTT AAA GCT TAT CCG GT 3'

   Mutation 2:
   5' TAC GGC CCC AGC TTA AAG CTT ATC CGG GT 3'

Chapter 9: Homeostasis: A Fine Balance

Organisms must constantly maintain their internal conditions to survive in their environment. The enzymes that control metabolism work at an optimal temperature range that is controlled by both behaviour and physiology. When many endothermic organisms become too warm, they dilate blood vessels in their extremities, causing more thermal energy to be lost to the surroundings. When many ectothermic organisms become too cold, they bask in the sun to absorb thermal energy from the environment. Water balance must also be maintained. This is often accomplished by osmoregulation and excretion of solutes in liquid waste. Many animals have elaborate excretory functions to regulate the concentrations of water, solutes and waste in the extracellular fluid. Negative feedback loops, in which an abundant product acts as an inhibitor to the process that creates it, are used to control homeostatic mechanisms.

BIG IDEAS

- Organisms have strict limits on the internal conditions that they can tolerate.
- Systems that maintain homeostasis rely on feedback mechanisms.
- Environmental factors can affect homeostasis.

Chapter 10: The Endocrine System

Hormones are chemical messengers that control body processes. Most hormones are made in one part of the body and carried by the blood stream to control other parts of the body, either a specific organ or a generalized effect. Protein hormones consist of amino acid chains and exert their effect by binding to receptors on cell membranes. Steroid hormones are derived from cholesterol, and exert their effect by binding to receptors in the cytosol. Both types of hormones are controlled by negative feedback mechanisms.

Growth, reproduction, and the concentration levels of many substances are controlled by hormones. For example, insulin, a protein hormone, is synthesized by the pancreas and reduces blood sugar levels. Impaired insulin secretion results in diabetes. Synthetic steroids have been developed to mimic the functions of natural steroids for medical applications and for enhanced athletic performance.

Hormone imbalances are being addressed by biotechnology in several ways, for example, by producing synthetic hormones such as insulin or by genetic engineering, which is still in the research stage.

Chapter 11: The Nervous System

Nerves (neurons) are living cells that use rapid, precise electrochemical impulses to control body functions and maintain homeostasis. Sensory neurons collect input from the environment and pass these signals to interneurons in the central nervous system for processing. Response signals are then carried to the appropriate muscles and glands by efferent neurons. All neurons receive electrochemical impulses through dendrites, and transmit electrochemical impulses through an axon. These impulses move across electrical or chemical synapses from one neuron to another.

Nervous responses can be voluntary and controlled by the somatic system, for example, touching your toes. Reflex loops enable even faster responses, for example pulling your hand away from a hot stove. The autonomic nervous system controls the involuntary actions of digestive, circulatory and respiratory muscles to control metabolic functions automatically.

The main organs of the central nervous system are the spinal cord and the brain. The human brain has evolved several specialized areas to allow for fast, accurate processing of information.

Maintaining an Internal Balance

Vocabulary	
homeostasis	interstitial fluid
internal environment	homeostatic mechanism

MAIN IDEA: Homeostasis is the process by which animals and plants maintain an internal environment that promotes proper cellular function. Homeostasis is an ongoing dynamic process that acts in response to both internal and external conditions.

1. Describe two changes that you experience in your external environment when you get up in the morning. Do you respond to these changes by altering your behaviour or do your internal systems make the adjustments? K/U T/I A

2. List two changes in your internal environment that you experience on a normal day. Do you respond to these changes by altering your behaviour or do your internal systems make the adjustments? K/U T/I

3. Why is it important for an organism to maintain homeostasis? T/I

4. Which of the following are responses to changing conditions that can help maintain homeostasis? Circle your answers. K/U
   (a) a cat curling up to sleep
   (b) a turtle sunning itself on a rock
   (c) a dog barking
   (d) the leaves of a plant releasing oxygen into the atmosphere
   (e) a girl putting on mittens
   (f) a family building a house

MAIN IDEA: The body's internal environment consists of the interstitial fluid that surrounds cells and tissues, and the plasma in the blood. Numerous organs and organ systems coordinate their activities to maintain homeostasis; however, the nervous and endocrine systems are the most important systems.

5. The interstitial fluid and the blood plasma make up a body's extracellular fluid. What is the function of the extracellular fluid? K/U

6. Complete **Table 1** to summarize the role different organ systems play in maintaining homeostasis. K/U T/I C

Table 1 Organ Systems Involved in Homeostasis

Organ system	Role in maintaining homeostasis
nervous system	
excretory system	
endocrine system	
immune system	
digestive system	
integumentary system	
circulatory system	

STUDY TIP

Review Previous Work
Concepts you studied in biology in previous grades can help you understand homeostasis. Review the organs in each organ system and their primary functions to help you understand how the systems work together to maintain homeostasis.

7. Why are the nervous system and the endocrine system described as the most important organ systems in maintaining homeostasis? Give specific examples of processes that these two organ systems regulate. K/U T/I

8. Use homeostasis to explain why each of the following events might occur. K/U A
   (a) We sweat when the temperature rises.

   (b) We become very thirsty after we eat salty foods.

   (c) Squirrels look fluffier in the winter.

Homeostasis and Feedback Mechanisms

Textbook pp. 432–435

Vocabulary

negative feedback	integrator	effector
sensor	set point	positive feedback

MAIN IDEA: Negative feedback occurs when a system responds to change by attempting to compensate for this change. A negative feedback mechanism has three components: a sensor, which detects changes in the body's conditions; an integrator, which compares the sensory information to the desired set point; and an effector, which acts to re-establish homeostasis.

1. A negative feedback loop restores normal conditions. Explain why it is described as 'negative' and give an example of a negative feedback loop in humans. K/U T/I

2. Use the flow chart below to identify the five stages of a negative feedback loop. K/U C

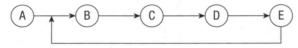

3. For each of the following examples of a negative feedback loop, suggest a sensor, an integrator, and an effector. K/U

   (a) You feel cold, so the blood vessels in your skin constrict to minimize the loss of thermal energy.

   (b) A driver sees the car is moving over the speed limit, so takes her foot off the accelerator.

   (c) You get a cut in your leg and begin to bleed.

4. Use the flow chart from question 2 to illustrate a negative feedback loop using the following labels: sweat gland, thermoreceptors in skin, sweat, thermoreceptors in hypothalamus, skin blood capillaries, increase in thermal energy. K/U C

MAIN IDEA: All animals use many negative feedback mechanisms to maintain homeostasis, and responses can be physiological or behavioural.

5. Which of the following types of organisms use feedback loops to regulate internal processes? Circle your answers. [K/U]

    (a) mammals

    (b) fish

    (c) insects

    (d) reptiles

    (e) plants

6. List four examples of negative feedback mechanisms in animals. Indicate whether each response is physiological or behavioural. [K/U] [T/I]

MAIN IDEA: Positive feedback mechanisms enhance the effect of a change in the internal or external environment, but usually do not result in homeostasis.

7. A positive feedback loop usually does not restore normal conditions. Explain why it is described as "positive." [K/U] [T/I]

8. (a) Describe an example of a positive feedback loop in humans.

    (b) In what way is the result of the example you described in part (a) *not* an example of homeostasis?

    (c) Why is it advantageous for the body to *not* be in homeostatic balance at certain times? [K/U] [T/I]

Thermoregulation

Textbook pp. 436–441

Vocabulary		
thermoregulation	endotherm	torpor
homeotherm	ectotherm	hibernation
poikilotherm	thermal acclimatization	estivation

Main idea: Thermal energy is transferred between animals and their environment by conduction, convection, radiation, and evaporation.

1. How is having a constant body temperature useful to an organism? K/U

2. Describe four ways an animal can lose thermal energy. K/U

3. Describe two ways an animal can gain thermal energy. K/U

Main idea: Homeotherms are animals that maintain a fairly constant internal temperature regardless of the external temperature. The internal body temperature of poikilotherms varies in response to the temperature of the external environment. Ectotherms are animals that regulate their body temperature by absorbing thermal energy from the environment. Endotherms are animals that regulate their body temperature with the internal mechanisms of thermal energy generation, conservation, and dissipation. Both endotherms and ectotherms have behavioural mechanisms that they can use to regulate their body temperature.

4. Describe similarities and differences between homeotherms and endotherms.
   K/U T/I

5. Describe similarities and differences between poikilotherms and ectotherms.
   K/U T/I

6. Describe advantages and disadvantages of controlling body temperature by behaviour. K/U T/I

7. Describe advantages and disadvantages of controlling body temperature by physiology. K/U T/I

8. Use **Table 1** to describe how endotherms and ectotherms respond to environmental temperature changes on a diurnal and seasonal scale. K/U T/I C

Table 1 Response to Temperature Change

	Endotherms	Ectotherms
Diurnal		
Seasonal		

9. Many animals are either endothermic homeotherms or ectothermic poikilotherms. List two examples of each group. K/U

10. A hummingbird is an endotherm, and can also be considered a poikilotherm. Why? K/U T/I

STUDY **TIP**

Prefixes and Suffixes
Examine suffixes and prefixes carefully to learn the meanings of words. *Ecto* means "outside", *endo* means "inside", and *homeo* means "the same as". How can knowing this help you understand endotherm, ectotherm, and homeotherm?

Main idea: Thermal acclimatization is the gradual adjustment to seasonal variations in temperature.

11. If the temperature is 15 °C in August, you feel cold and put on extra clothing but if the temperature is 15 °C in April, you feel hot and put on shorts. Why do you think the same temperature can have opposite effects on the body. K/U T/I

12. Describe an example of an ectotherm using thermal acclimatization adaptations. K/U

Water Balance

Textbook pp. 442–445

> **Vocabulary**
>
> osmotic pressure   hypoosmotic   osmoregulation
>
> hyperosmotic   isoosmotic

MAIN IDEA: Osmoregulation ensures that the intracellular and extracellular fluids are isoosmotic, and it keeps the internal concentrations of water and ions different from the concentrations in the external environment.

1. Why would an animal that lives in an aqueous environment, such as a salmon, have to regulate water uptake and expulsion? K/U

2. Complete **Table 1** to compare the characteristics of hyperosmotic, hypoosmotic and isoosmotic solutions. K/U T/I C

Table 1 Characteristics of Solutions

	Hyperosmotic	**Hypoosmotic**	**Isoosmotic**
Concentration of water			
Concentration of solutes			
Direction of water diffusion			
Direction of solute diffusion			

3. (a) Discuss the pressures in the cell that cause water to enter the cell.

   (b) Discuss the pressures in the cell that cause water to leave the cell. K/U

4. Why do plants sometimes wilt on a hot dry day? K/U A

MAIN IDEA: Osmoregulation is closely linked to the process of excretion, in which animals expel waste products of metabolism to the external environment. The excretory system removes nitrogenous waste, excess water, and toxic compounds from the body. The main organs in the excretory system are the liver and the kidney.

5. Distinguish between the terms excretion and secretion. Include an example of each. K/U

6. How do diffusion, osmosis, and excretion work together to maintain homeostasis in an organism? K/U T/I

7. Do all animals have bladders? Explain. K/U T/I

8. In addition to water concentrations, what other two factors does excretion help animals keep in balance? K/U

9. One of the main waste products we produce is ammonia. Where does this type of waste come from and why is it important for our bodies to eliminate it? K/U

10. What challenge does elimination pose for many terrestrial animals? K/U

11. Draw a flow chart to show how nitrogenous waste is created and then excreted in mammals. K/U C

The Excretory System

Vocabulary

contractile vacuole	afferent arteriole	distal convoluted tubule
metanephridium	efferent arteriole	filtration
Malpighian tubule	peritubular capillaries	reabsorption
nephron	proximal convoluted tubule	aquaporin
Bowman's capsule	loop of Henle	secretion
glomerulus		

MAIN IDEA: Single-celled organisms excrete waste directly to the environment. Most invertebrates have specialized structures to process and excrete waste.

1. Discuss the osmotic pressures on a protozoan and a mechanism that regulates these pressures. [K/U] [T/I]

2. Discuss the role of the metanephridia and the Malpighian tubules, and their importance in storing waste in the organism's body. [K/U]

MAIN IDEA: The Bowman's capsule and the glomerulus filter the blood. The fluid then moves through the proximal convoluted tubule, which actively reabsorbs ions and nutrients. Additional water is removed passively. The filtered blood reabsorbs water, ions, and other molecules, which are then absorbed in the peritubular capillaries. In the descending portion of the loop of Henle, water is reabsorbed by osmosis. In the ascending portion of the loop, ions are removed via active transport. In the distal convoluted tubule, the salt concentrations of the filtrate and the interstitial fluid are balanced. In the collecting duct additional water is reabsorbed. The urine is collected in the renal pelvis. From there, it flows into the bladder, where it is stored until it is excreted.

3. Label the parts of the kidney nephron shown in **Figure 1** below.

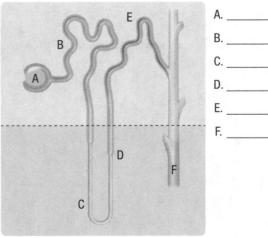

A. _____

B. _____

C. _____

D. _____

E. _____

F. _____

Figure 1

STUDY TIP

Using Diagrams and Descriptions
As you follow the path of waste through the kidney diagram at right, desribe what happens in each part of the kidney.

4. Complete **Table 1** to compare the relative concentrations of plasma, filtrate, and urine in the kidney. Use these terms: low, medium, high, variable, none. K/U T/I

Table 1 Fluids in the Kidney

	Glomerulus	Bowman's capsule	Collecting tubule
Water concentration			
Glucose concentration			
Amino acid concentration			
Sodium chloride concentration			
Urea concentration			
Oxygen concentration			
Carbon dioxide concentration			
Plasma proteins			
Cells			

5. Use **Table 2** to summarize the main points of the three stages of urine formation. K/U T/I

Table 2 Urine Formation

	Filtration	Reabsorption	Secretion
Location(s)			
Materials moving into blood and body			
Materials moving out of blood and body			
Active transport involved?			
Passive transport involved?			

Main Idea: There are many diseases and disorders that can interfere with the proper functioning of the kidneys in excreting wastes and maintaining water balance.

6. Suggest possible problems that could develop in an organ that concentrates the body's wastes. K/U T/I

7. Suggest possible problems that could develop in an organ that contains large numbers of blood capillaries, some under pressure. K/U T/I

Homeostasis: A Fine Balance

Complete the flow chart that illustrates two examples of homeostatic control mechanisms using a negative feedback loop.

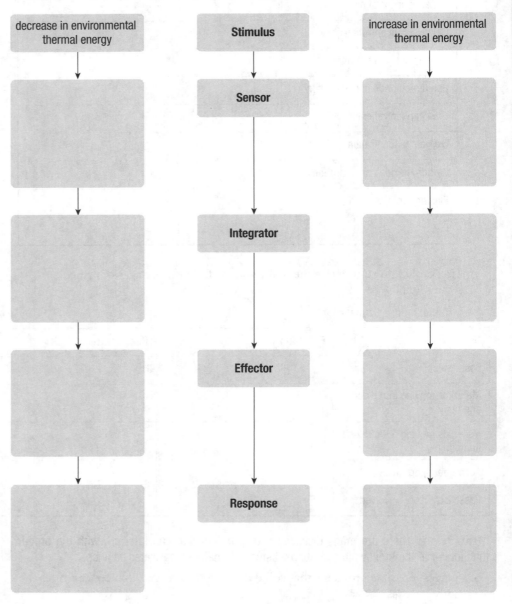

1. When the ambient (room) temperature is very high, such as 32 °C, the body will lose thermal energy through which mechanism? (9.3) K/U
   (a) radiation
   (b) conduction
   (c) evaporation
   (d) increased metabolism

K/U   Knowledge/Understanding
T/I   Thinking/Investigation
C   Communication
A   Application

Table 1 shows a patient's test results. Use Table 1 to answer questions 2 and 3.

Table 1 Composition of fluids in kidney (g/100 mL)

Substance	Component	Plasma	Filtrate	Urine
U	urea	0.030	0.030	2.00
V	uric acid	0.004	0.004	0.05
W	glucose	0.100	0.100	0.00
X	amino acids	0.050	0.050	0.00
Y	salts	0.720	0.720	1.50
Z	proteins	8.000	0.036	0.00

2. Which substances were completely reabsorbed into the plasma? (9.5) K/U T/I
   (a) U, V, Y   (b) W, Y, Z   (c) U, W, X   (d) W, X, Z

3. Which substances were excreted? (9.5) K/U T/I
   (a) U, V, Y   (b) W, Y, Z   (c) U, W, X   (d) W, X, Z

4. A family doctor has a patient with the following symptoms: very high blood sugar levels; high sugar level in the urine; constant thirst; produces large quantities of urine. Which condition should the doctor investigate? (9.5) K/U T/I
   (a) diabetes insipidus
   (b) Bright's disease
   (c) diabetes mellitus
   (d) kidney stones

5. Indicate whether each statement is true or false. If you think a statement is false, rewrite it to make it true. K/U
   (a) Some animals sun themselves or retreat to shade as a way of regulating their body temperature. (9.2)

   (b) Kidneys remove waste, balance blood pH, and maintain water balance. (9.4)

   (c) Wastes are filtered from the blood by the kidneys and conducted to the urinary bladder by the urethra. (9.5)

6. The nitrogen that mammals excrete comes from what source? (9.4) K/U

7. Which environment is more dangerous to an endotherm: one above its critical temperature or one below its critical temperature? Explain. (9.3) K/U T/I

8. How do you think the quantity of urine formed by a frog would change when the frog moves from a pond onto land? Would the quantity of urine formed by a beaver change under the same circumstances? Explain your answer. (9.5) K/U T/I A

9. Imagine you are playing an active game and you begin to sweat. Soon you feel cooler. Construct a labelled diagram to represent the feedback loop involved in this homeostatic system. On the diagram, indicate the receptor(s), the control centre(s), and the effector(s). (9.2) K/U T/I C

10. Complete **Table 2** to compare the concentrations of substances found in the excretion of urine by a healthy person's kidneys. (9.5) K/U C

Table 2 Substance Concentration

Substance	Blood of the afferent arteriole	Bowman's capsule filtrate	Urine
blood protein			
glucose			
sodium ions			
urea			

11. Describe how each process below is involved in the removal of nitrogenous wastes by a human nephron. (9.5) K/U
    (a) filtration

    (b) reabsorption

    (c) active transport:

Hormones: Chemical Regulators

Vocabulary

protein hormone   steroid hormone

Textbook pp. 468–472

MAIN IDEA: Most hormones are chemicals secreted by the cells of the endocrine system that control the activities of cells elsewhere in the body. Most hormones are either protein hormones or steroid hormones. Protein hormones are water-soluble and tend to bind to plasma membrane receptors. Steroid hormones are lipids and not as water-soluble, but they pass easily through the plasma membrane and tend to attach to receptors inside the cell.

1. Use **Table 1** to compare protein hormones and steroid hormones. K/U C

   Table 1 Protein Hormones versus Steroid Hormones

	Protein hormone	**Steroid hormone**
Composition		
Solubility		
Interactions at plasma membrane		
Major examples		

2. How are hormones removed from the body? K/U

MAIN IDEA: Only target cells that have the correct receptor proteins respond to the presence of a specific hormone. Once a receptor protein is bound to a hormone, it signals other proteins inside the cell to turn certain cellular processes on or off.

3. Label **Figure 1** to show how a hormone binds to a receptor inside the cell. Describe the events that occur at sites 1, 2 and 3. K/U C

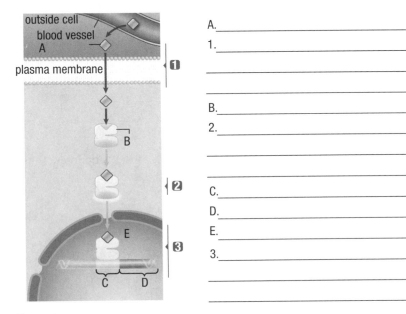

A._____

1._____

_____

_____

B._____

2._____

_____

_____

C._____

D._____

E._____

3._____

_____

_____

Figure 1

---

4. Label **Figure 2** to show how a hormone binds to a receptor in the plasma membrane. Describe the events that occur at sites 1, 2 and 3. K/U C

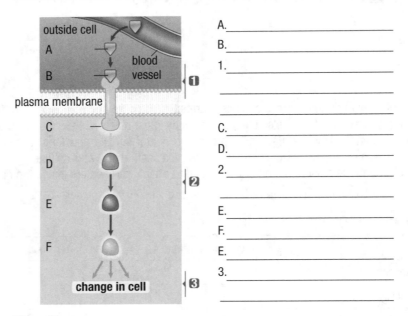

A._____

B._____

1._____

_____

_____

C._____

D._____

2._____

_____

E._____

F._____

E._____

3._____

_____

Figure 2

MAIN IDEA: Many hormones are controlled by negative feedback mechanisms. In a negative feedback mechanism, the increasing concentration of a chemical turns off further production of a hormone. The glands of the endocrine system and their hormones work together to control other body systems and maintain homeostasis.

5. Identify the parts of the flow chart to illustrate an example of a hormone negative feedback loop. K/U C

_____ hypothalamus   _____ thyroid hormones   _____ TSH

_____ pituitary   _____ TRH

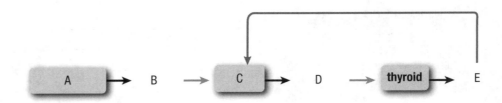

6. Identify the sensor, integrator, and effector in the feedback loop in question 4. T/I

The Endocrine Glands

Vocabulary

hypothalamus	pituitary gland	parathyroid hormone
neurohormone	thyroid gland	pineal gland

Textbook pp. 473–482

MAIN IDEA: The endocrine system of glands and the hormones they produce regulate bodily processes, maintain homeostasis, and control growth, development, and reproduction.

1. Label the major human endocrine glands shown in **Figure 1**. K/U C

STUDY TIP

Prefixes
Prefixes can help you remember the names of glands. For example, *hypo-* means "above," *para-* means "around," and *ad-* means "on".

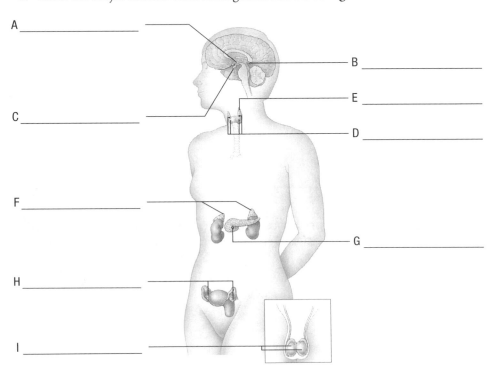

A _____

B _____

E _____

C _____

D _____

F _____

G _____

H _____

I _____

Figure 1

2. In addition to the main endocrine glands shown in Figure 1 above, what other organs in the human body produce important hormones? K/U

MAIN IDEA: The hypothalamus and pituitary gland control other endocrine glands throughout the body. The hypothalamus responds to messages from the brain or nerve receptors by releasing hormones. These hormones control the pituitary gland's secretion of other hormones, which regulate the rest of the endocrine system.

3. Describe two conditions caused by a malfunction in two different endocrine glands. Explain in detail what has gone wrong in each case. K/U

4. Complete **Table 1** to describe one hormone produced by each endocrine gland and its function. K/U C

Table 1 Endocrine Gland Hormones

Endocrine gland	Hormone	Function
hypothalamus		
anterior pituitary gland		
posterior pituitary gland		
thyroid gland		
parathyroid gland		
adrenal glands		
pineal gland		

MAIN IDEA: Many of the hormones found in vertebrates are also found in invertebrates, although their functions may differ. Hormones in invertebrates control metamorphosis, moulting, and reproduction.

5. The hormones ecdysone and juvenile hormone control moulting in insects. Explain how these two hormones work together. K/U

6. Crustaceans also shed their exoskeleton as they grow. Compare the roles that hormones play in crustacean moulting with the roles that hormones play in insect moulting. K/U T/I

Regulating Blood Sugar

Vocabulary	
islets of Langerhans	glucagon

Textbook pp. 483–487

MAIN IDEA: The islets of Langerhans in the pancreas secrete insulin, which lowers the blood glucose level, and glucagon, which raises the blood glucose level. The balance of insulin and glucagon regulates the concentration of glucose in the blood.

1. For each function of the pancreas in **Table 1** below, identify the source of the function and describe each process. K/U C

Table 1 Functions of the Pancreas

Function	Source	Process
secretion of digestive enzymes		
lower blood sugar levels		
raise blood sugar levels		

2. You eat a meal with a high sugar content. Explain how each factor below will respond and why. K/U T/I
   (a) blood sugar

   (b) alpha cells

   (c) beta cells

> **STUDY TIP**
>
> **Review Prior Learning**
> Insulin and glucagon are part of negative feedback mechanisms. Review negative feedback mechanisms in Chapter 9 and in Section 10.1.

3. You have not eaten a meal after several hours of exercise. How will each factor below respond and why? K/U T/I
   (a) blood sugar

   (b) alpha cells

   (c) beta cells

4. What are some symptoms of hypoglycemia and of hyperglycemia? K/U

MAIN IDEA: Diabetes mellitus is a disease in which the blood glucose level is not properly regulated due to a failure of insulin production or action. Type 1 diabetes is caused by an inability to produce insulin, due to a failure of beta cells in the islets of Langerhans. It tends to develop during childhood. Type 2 diabetes is caused by insulin insufficiency and/or by the inability of cells to respond correctly to insulin. It tends to develop during adulthood, often as a result of obesity.

5. Draw a flow chart to illustrate how diabetes can result in excess thirst. K/U C

6. Describe three serious effects of diabetes. K/U

7. Complete **Table 2** to compare type 1 and type 2 diabetes. K/U C

Table 2 Diabetes Comparison

	Type 1 Diabetes	**Type 2 Diabetes**
Onset		
Possible cause(s)		
Most effective treatments		
Possibility of cure		

8. Why do you think more intensive treatment is often required to manage type 1 diabetes than type 2 diabetes? T/I

Biology JOURNAL

Insulin: A Miracle Discovery

Textbook pp. 488–489

MAIN IDEA: Banting and Best's initial trials on dogs failed but led them to other conclusions that helped them to discover insulin in 1922.

1. Previous scientists had shown that if the pancreas of a dog is removed, the dog contracts diabetes. What hypotheses did Banting and Best propose to clarify this finding? K/U

2. (a) What did Banting and Best believe caused the dog in their first experiment to develop diabetes?

   (b) How did they learn that the diabetes they observed was not caused by the mechanism you described in part (a)? K/U T/I

> **STUDY TIP**
>
> **Unsupported Hypothesis**
> You can learn just as much, if not more, from a hypothesis that your experimental data does not support as you can from a hypothesis that your experimental data does support.

3. Why do you think the dog that Banting and Best removed the pancreas from and injected insulin into eventually died? T/I

4. (a) Describe the difficulties that needed to be overcome before giving insulin to humans.

   (b) How did Banting and Best overcome the difficulties you described in part (a)? K/U

5. Describe how modern biotechnology has contributed to the issue of diabetes treatments. K/U

Steroids: Natural and Synthetic

Vocabulary		
estrogens	progestins	synthetic hormone

MAIN IDEA: Steroids belong to a category of lipids that includes several hormones that act on receptors inside cells. Natural steroid hormones occur in the human body and control both male and female sexual development and reproduction, the adrenal fight-or-flight response, and the blood glucose level.

1. Complete the following description of the interaction between the steroid hormone receptor and the steroid hormone response element. [K/U]

   The _____ is a protein in the _____ of the cell. It has a specific _____ that will be activated when the matching _____ enters the cell. The steroid hormone receptor binds to the _____ and transports it into the _____.

   The _____ is a DNA element adjacent to the _____ whose expression is controlled by the _____.

   The _____ binds to the _____

   _____, which activates transcription of the

   _____, resulting in the production of _____.

2. Complete **Table 1** to summarize the functions of natural steroids and their value to athletes. [K/U] [T/I] [C] [A]

Table 1 Natural Steroids

Steroid	Function	Value to athlete
testosterone		
cortisol		

MAIN IDEA: There are many legitimate medical uses of synthetic steroids, including as painkillers and anti-inflammatories such as those found in asthma inhalers. Steroid use should only be for a valid medical reason, and must be supervised by a physician.

3. Describe the interaction of a synthetic hormone and a steroid hormone receptor. [K/U] [T/I]

4. Complete **Table 2** to summarize the uses and side effects of synthetic hormones. K/U T/I C

Table 2 Synthetic Steroids

Steroid	prednisone	beclomethasone	dexmethasone	hydrocortisone
Therapeutic use				
Possible side effects				

MAIN IDEA: There are many uses of synthetic steroids that are banned in the world of sports. The long-term use of synthetic steroids can lead to baldness, shrinking testes, irregular reproductive cycles, and many other physical and psychological side effects.

5. Use what you know about the effects of each hormone in Question 4 to predict what value it may have to an athlete's performance in competition. K/U T/I

6. On a separate sheet of paper, construct a Venn diagram to classify potential side effects of the long-term use of anabolic steroids as particular to males, particular to females, or common to both. K/U T/I C

7. Complete **Table 3** to show how athletes can improve their performance with and without using synthetic steroids. K/U T/I C A

Table 3 Improved Athletic Performance

Desired effect	With synthetic steroids	Without synthetic steroids
increased muscle mass		
increased oxygen supply		
increased reaction time		
increased endurance		
decreased pain levels		

Textbook pp. 494–495

The Cost of Performance-Enhancing Drug Use

MAIN IDEA: Performance-enhancing drug use comes with a heavy physical and social cost.

1. Performance-enhancing drug use by athletes is believed to be both unfair and widespread. Decide whether you agree or disagree with each statement below and justify your opinion. K/U T/I C

(a) Using performance-enhancing drugs is just another example of how athletes bend or break rules in sport so it's not really an issue.

(b) The ban is unfair because it is hard to differentiate natural hormones from synthetic hormones.

(c) The ban is unfair because natural hormone levels vary so one athlete might test positive while another tests negative after using the same banned hormone.

(d) Banning athletes from using painkillers and cold medicines is unfair because people in other professions can use them when they are working.

(e) Athletes are allowed to use drugs, such as alcohol and nicotine, which have proven health risks, so banning performance-enhancing drugs on health grounds is hypocritical.

The Reproductive Hormones

Vocabulary

gonads

androgens

gonadotropin-releasing
  hormone (GnRH)

oogenesis

menopause

menstrual cycle

testosterone

spermatogenesis

Textbook pp. 496–503

MAIN IDEA: Reproduction is controlled by the sex hormones, which are primarily produced in the gonads: the testes in males and the ovaries in females.

1. Label the reproductive organs shown in **Figure 1**. K/U C

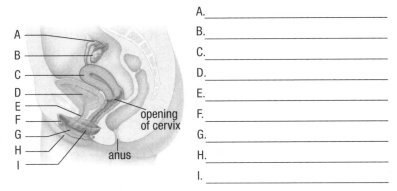

A._____

B._____

C._____

D._____

E._____

F._____

G._____

H._____

I._____

Figure 1 Female Reproductive Organs

2. Label the reproductive organs shown in **Figure 2**. K/U C

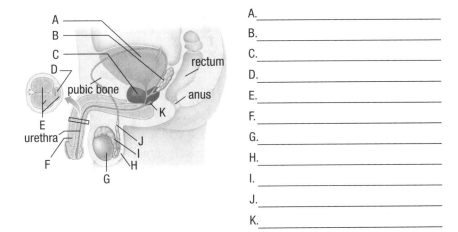

A._____

B._____

C._____

D._____

E._____

F._____

G._____

H._____

I._____

J._____

K._____

Figure 2 Male Reproductive Organs

MAIN IDEA: Testosterone is the primary sex hormone in males, and estrogen is the primary sex hormone in females. These hormones control the development of the secondary sex characteristics and the sex drive.

3. What triggers the synthesis of testosterone in males? Compare this to the trigger for the synthesis of estrogen in females. K/U T/I

4. Complete **Table 1** to summarize the roles played by testosterone and estrogen. K/U C

Table 1 Roles of Testosterone and Estrogen

	Testosterone	Estrogen
Source		
Target structure or cells		
Gender primarily affected		
Main functions		

MAIN IDEA: Follicle-stimulating hormone (FSH) is released by the pituitary gland in response to gonadotropin-releasing hormones (GnRH) from the hypothalamus. FSH stimulates the development of oocytes in the ovary. Ova (eggs) are produced from oocytes in a process called oogenesis.

5. Complete the paragraph to describe the process of fertilization. K/U

_____ hormone from the _____ causes _____ secretion in the _____, leading to _____, which starts _____ secretion. The egg descends into the _____ where it is fertilized by a _____. The first cell divisions of the _____ occur in the _____ then, after about seven days, the _____ is implanted in the _____. The cells secrete _____ _____ to keep the _____ in the ovary from breaking down. Continued activity of the corpus luteum keeps _____ and _____ secretion at high levels, which maintains the _____ and prevents _____.

6. Complete **Table 2** to summarize the roles of follicle-stimulating hormone, luteinizing hormone, and progesterone in the menstrual cycle and the ovarian cycle. K/U T/I C

Table 2 Female Hormones

	FSH	LH	Progesterone
Source			
Target structure or cell			
Main function			

MAIN IDEA: Spermatogenesis, the production of sperm in the testes of the male, is controlled by the male androgen hormone testosterone. Males produce sperm constantly, at a rate of about 130 million per day.

7. Complete the summary of spermatogenesis. K/U

   Spermatogenesis takes place in the _____ tubules in the _____. The developing spermatocytes are surrounded by _____ cells, which supply _____ and seal off the spermatocytes from the body's _____ supply. _____ cells produce testosterone and other androgens. Mature sperm move into the _____ and from there into the _____, a thick-walled, muscular tube.

8. Complete the flow chart to illustrate two negative feedback mechanisms involved in the synthesis of testosterone. K/U T/I C

MAIN IDEA: The hormones estrogen and progesterone carefully control the menstrual cycle to go along with the ovarian cycle and prepare the body for pregnancy. The manipulation of hormones in females can be used to control reproduction.

9. How does hormonal birth control mimic the function of female reproductive hormones? K/U T/I A

10. Describe six side effects of hormonal birth control. Classify them as common, uncommon, or rare. K/U

11. Why is any hormonal medication an environmental issue? K/U T/I

The Endocrine System

The reproductive hormones in males and females demonstrates the concept of control by negative feedback. Complete the following flow chart.

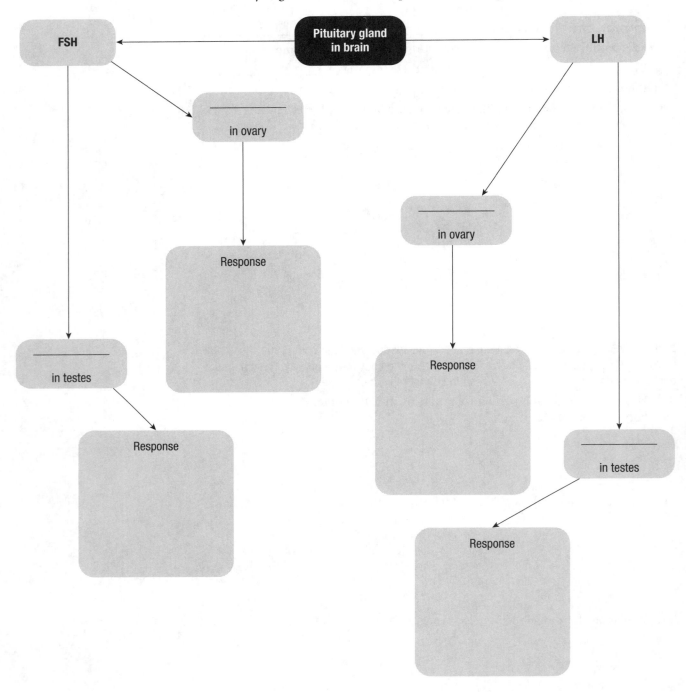

K/U Knowledge/Understanding
T/I Thinking/Investigation
C   Communication
A   Application

1. Which factor is controlled by ADH? (10.2) K/U
   (a) the level of glucose in the blood
   (b) the amount of water re-absorbed in the nephron
   (c) the development of the lining of the uterus
   (d) the release of an ovum from the ovary

2. Anti-diuretic hormone is secreted by which organ? (10.2) K/U
   (a) thyroid   (c) pituitary gland
   (b) adrenal glands   (d) hypothalamus

3. Indicate whether each statement is true or false. If you think a statement is false, rewrite it to make it true. K/U
   (a) After other scientists showed that dogs without a pancreas developed diabetes, Frederick Banting and Charles Best isolated a factor they called isletin that reversed the dogs' symptoms. (10.4)

   (b) Large amounts of hormone are required to cause change. (10.1)

   (c) Insulin is produced in a healthy person when blood sugar is low. (10.3)

   (d) People with diabetes feel tired because of low levels of glucose in the blood. (10.3)

   (e) Both males and females synthesize GnRH, FSH, and LH. (10.7)

4. What condition is caused by insufficient production of ADH? (10.2) K/U

5. Three patients are under observation for a period of 10 days. **Table 1** shows the medical assessment for each patient. (10.2) K/U T/I

   Table 1 Patient Test Results

	Mr. Janvier	Mr. Yamamoto	Ms. Desai
Urine produced/day	1.5 L	13 L	0.2 L
Sweat	normal	above normal	none
Thirst	normal	intense	none

   (a) Which patient has hyposecretion of the pituitary gland?

   (b) Which patient has hypersecretion of the pituitary gland?

6. Mrs. Schwartz has lost a lot of weight, has a low blood calcium level and protruding eyes, is easily agitated, and always feels cold. What condition could cause these symptoms? (10.2) K/U T/I

7. Metabolic homeostasis concerns the thyroid gland. The thyroid is regulated by feedback loops involving which of the following? (10.1) K/U
   (a) the pituitary gland and two hormones
   (b) the hypothalamus, pancreas and four hormones
   (c) the hypothalamus, the pituitary gland and three hormones
   (d) the islets of Langerhans and three hormones

8. Complete the sentences below to explain how hormones work. (10.1) K/U
   Hormones attach to specific cells by their _____.
   _____ hormones attach to receptors within the cytoplasm.
   _____ hormones attach to receptors on the cell membrane.

9. During an allergic response to a bee sting or pollen, which hormone is often released? (10.2) K/U

10. What is an indicator that a person's thyroid gland has malfunctioned and failed to secrete sufficient thyroxine? (10.2) K/U

11. How does adrenaline affect the flow of blood? (10.2) K/U

12. Give an example of a hormone that regulates a positive feedback mechanism. (10.2) K/U

13. Long term stress is harmful and often results in higher blood sugar levels. List three complications that may result from having a high blood sugar level. (10.3) K/U

14. List three side effects of taking anabolic steroids. (10.6) K/U

15. Where is the primary production site of progesterone? (10.7) K/U

16. Provide an example of a hormone that is non-target in behaviour and explain why this is necessary. (10.3) K/U

17. People who have severe allergies to bee stings or peanuts usually carry a syringe with a solution of adrenaline. How does this help them recover from an allergic reaction? (10.2) K/U T/I A

18. Why are some performance-enhancing drugs difficult to detect in athletes? Provide two examples. (10.6) K/U

The Role of the Nervous System

Vocabulary

neuron	glial cell	somatic system
neural signalling	myelin sheath	autonomic system
afferent neuron	node of Ranvier	sympathetic division
interneuron	central nervous system (CNS)	parasympathetic division
efferent neuron	peripheral nervous system (PNS)	neural circuit
dendrite	afferent system	reflex arc
axon	efferent system	

Textbook pp. 516–521

MAIN IDEA: The nervous system of an animal has four main functions: (1) it receives information about conditions in the internal and external environment; (2) it transmits messages along neurons; (3) it integrates the information to formulate an appropriate response; and (4) it sends signals to effector tissues or organs. Neurons are cells that are specialized for the reception and transmission of electrical signals.

1. What part of a neuron is involved in each activity? K/U

   (a) synthesizing proteins, carbohydrates, and lipids for cell use

   (b) receiving external stimuli

   (c) bundling together to form nerves, which transmit signals over long distances

   (d) passing signals to other cells

STUDY TIP

Make Connections
As you learn about the characteristics of various components of the nervous system, always consider how those characteristics help that component carry out one of these functions.

2. Label **Figure 1** to show the parts of a neuron. Add arrows to show the direction of the electrical impulses that travel across a neuron. K/U C

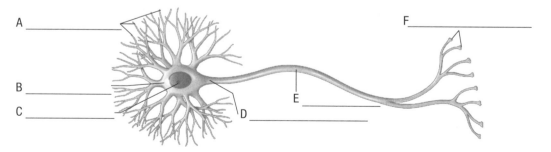

A _____

B _____

C _____

D _____

E _____

F _____

Figure 1

MAIN IDEA: Afferent neurons conduct information from sensory receptors to interneurons, which integrate the information into a response. The response signals are passed to efferent neurons, which activate the effectors that perform the response. A neural circuit consists of the receptor, the afferent neuron, the interneuron, the efferent neuron, and the effector. The simplest neural circuit is the reflex arc.

3. Complete **Table 1** to summarize how neurons process information in the nervous system. K/U C

Table 1 Neural Signalling

Component	Type of nerve	Action of neural signal
reception		
transmission		
integration		
response		

4. Label the parts of a reflex arc shown in **Figure 2.** K/U C

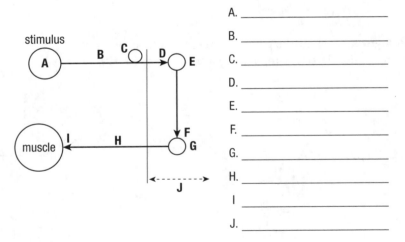

A. _____

B. _____

C. _____

D. _____

E. _____

F. _____

G. _____

H. _____

I. _____

J. _____

Figure 2

MAIN IDEA: The central nervous system (CNS) consists of the brain and spinal cord. It communicates with the peripheral nervous system (PNS), which is made up of the afferent and efferent systems.

5. Which part of the nervous system is used to process information related to each area below? K/U

   (a) senses

   (b) voluntary actions

   (c) involuntary actions that speed up respiratory metabolism

   (d) involuntary actions that slow down respiratory metabolism

6. Label the main parts of the nervous system shown in **Figure 3.** K/U C

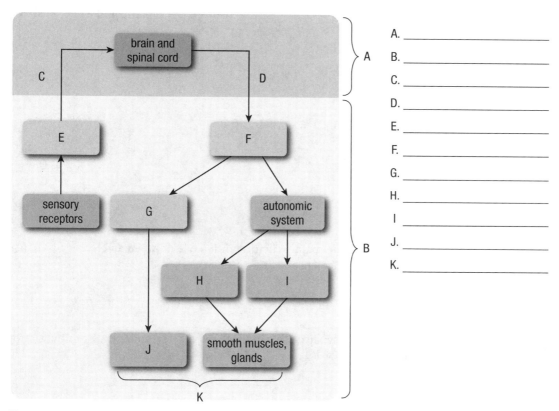

A. _____

B. _____

C. _____

D. _____

E. _____

F. _____

G. _____

H. _____

I _____

J. _____

K. _____

Figure 3

MAIN IDEA: Glial cells provide structural and functional support to neurons. They help to maintain the balance of ions surrounding the neurons and form insulating layers around the axons.

7. What characteristics of neurons makes them vulnerable? In what ways would they benefit from structural and functional support? K/U T/I

8. What are the myelin sheath and nodes of Ranvier? How do they support neurons? K/U

Nerve Signals

Textbook pp. 522–529

Vocabulary

synapse	synaptic cleft	ion channel	threshold potential
chemical synapse	electrical synapse	resting potential	refractory period
neurotransmitter	membrane potential	action potential	

MAIN IDEA: Neurons make connections using two types of synapses: electrical and chemical. In an electrical synapse, impulses pass directly from the sending cell to the receiving cell by ion flow through gap junctions. In chemical synapses, neurotransmitters released from the presynaptic cell bind to the postsynaptic cell.

1. (a) Draw and label a diagram of an electrical synapse and a chemical synapse.

   (b) What are the main structural difference between an electrical synapse and a chemical synapse? K/U C

2. Which type of synapse do you think would transmit impulses signals more quickly? Why? K/U A

MAIN IDEA: The unequal distribution of positive and negative charges on either side of a neuron's membrane establishes a potential difference, called the resting potential. An action potential is generated when a stimulus pushes the resting potential to the threshold value at which Na^+ channels open in the plasma membrane. Action potentials move along an axon as the ion flows generated in one location on the axon depolarize the potential in an adjacent location.

3. What advantage does a chemical synapse have over an electrical synapse? K/U

4. Number the steps below to show the correct sequence for signal transmission in a chemical synapse. K/U T/I

___ neurotransmitter binds with receptor

___ calcium ions rush into neuron's cytoplasm

___ action potential depolarizes the presynaptic membrane

___ ion gate opens to allow particular ion to enter cell

___ synaptic vesicles release neurotransmitter into the synaptic cleft

Use **Figure 1** to answer questions 5 to 7.

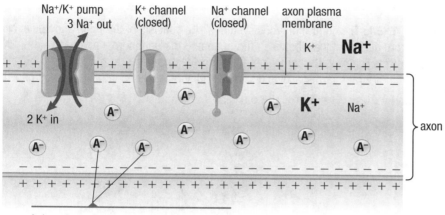

Figure 1

5. Describe the concentrations of the ions inside and outside the neural membrane during resting potential. K/U

STUDY **TIP**

Review Prior Knowledge
To help you understand the role K^+ and Na^+ play in transmitting neural impulses, review how ions interact in Chapter 1.

6. Describe the concentrations of the ions inside and outside the neural membrane during action potential. K/U

7. Describe the concentrations of the ions inside and outside the neural membrane during the refractory period. K/U

NEL

11.2 Nerve Signals **163**

The Central Nervous System

Textbook pp. 530–536

Vocabulary

meninges	medulla oblongata	cerebral cortex
cerebrospinal fluid	cerebellum	thalamus
grey matter	pons	blood–blood barrier
white matter	cerebrum	

MAIN IDEA: The central nervous system (CNS) consists of the brain and spinal cord. The spinal cord carries signals between the brain and the peripheral nervous system (PNS) and also controls reflexes. Cerebrospinal fluid provides nutrients to the CNS and cushions the CNS. A blood-brain barrier allows only selected substances to enter the cerebrospinal fluid.

1. Label **Figure 1** to show the parts of the spinal cord. K/U C

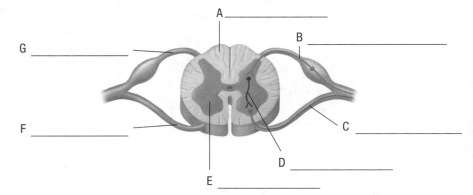

A _____

B _____

G _____

F _____

C _____

D _____

E _____

Figure 1

2. Label **Figure 2** to show the parts of the brain. K/U C

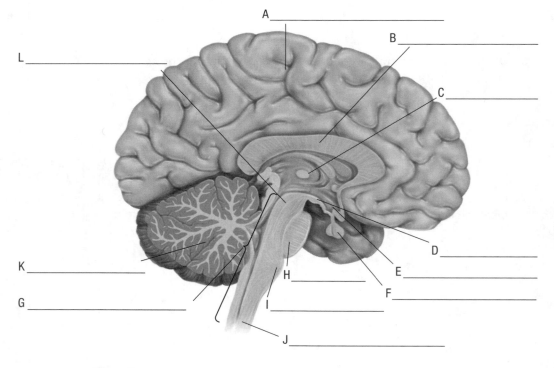

A _____

B _____

C _____

L _____

D _____

E _____

F _____

K _____

G _____

H _____

I _____

J _____

Figure 2

3. (a) Describe possible problems that could arise from the diffusion of blood contents into the cerebral fluids in the brain.

(b) How is the brain protected from this danger? K/U

MAIN IDEA: The primary somatosensory areas of the cerebral cortex register incoming sensory information. The primary motor areas of the cerebrum control voluntary movements of skeletal muscles in the body. Some functions, including long-term memory and consciousness, are equally distributed between the two cerebral hemispheres. Other functions are concentrated in the left hemisphere or the right hemisphere.

4. In **Table 1** below, describe six different functions that would be processed in the cerebral cortex. Indicate in which area of the cortex each function would be processed. An example has been provided. K/U T/I C A

Table 1 Processing in the Cerebrum

Function	Processed in what part of cerebral cortex?
moving fingers to write with a pencil	primary somatosensory area

5. Complete the following description of the two cerebral hemispheres. K/U

Each cerebral _____ can function separately. The

right _____ responds primarily to

_____ signals from, and controls _____ in,

the _____ side of the body. It also specializes in _____

conceptualizing, including _____, and _____ recognition.

The left _____ responds primarily to

_____ signals from, and controls _____ in, the

_____ side of the body and also specializes in spoken and written

_____ , _____ reasoning, and _____.

_____ bundles called the _____ connect

the two hemispheres.

6. The surface layer of the human cerebrum is intricately folded and contains many unmyelinated neurons. How might that be advantageous to the complex processing that goes on there? K/U T/I

MAIN IDEA: Grey-matter centres in the pons and medulla control involuntary functions, such as heart rate, blood pressure, respiration rate, and digestion. Centres in the midbrain coordinate responses to visual and auditory sensory input.

7. Complete **Table 2** to summarize the functions of the following structures in the midbrain and hind brain. K/U C

Table 2 Midbrain and Hindbrain

Brain area	Function
cerebellum	
thalamus	
hypothalamus	
pituitary gland	
basal nuclei	

8. In what ways do the structures of the midbrain and hindbrain work with the cerebrum to carry out their functions? K/U A

9. The midbrain and hindbrain function together with the endocrine system to maintain homeostasis. Identify which part of the brain is most involved in this coordinated effort and describe the interaction. K/U T/I

The Peripheral Nervous System

Textbook pp. 537–541

Vocabulary

spinal nerves cranial nerves substantia gelatinosa (SG)

MAIN IDEA: The somatic system of the peripheral nervous system (PNS) controls the skeletal muscles that produce voluntary body movements, as well as the involuntary muscle contractions that maintain balance, posture, and muscle tone.

1. The somatic system consists of 31 pairs of spinal nerves, controlling different parts of the body. Complete **Table 1** to identify the parts of the body controlled by each type of spinal nerve. K/U C

Table 1 Spinal Nerves

Type of spinal nerve	Area of body controlled

2. Complete the following description of how the spinal nerves emanate from the spinal column. K/U

The _____ roots, which lay outside the spinal cord, form the

beginning of the _____ nervous system. Each _____

nerve branches repeatedly. In mammals, _____ exit from

the spinal cord in the _____ root to carry efferent signals to the

_____ muscles. The _____ and _____ of

the motor neurons are located _____ the spinal cord. Their _____

extend from the spinal cord to the _____ cells they

control.

MAIN IDEA: The autonomic system of the PNS controls involuntary functions, such as heart rate, blood pressure, glandular secretions, and smooth muscle contractions. The autonomic system is organized into sympathetic and parasympathetic divisions, which balance and fine-tune involuntary body functions. The sympathetic system predominates in situations of stress, danger, or strenuous activities. The parasympathetic system predominates during quiet, low-stress situations.

3. On a separate sheet of paper, draw a Venn diagram to compare the structure of the autonomic nervous sytem with the structure of the somatic nervous system. K/U C

4. Complete **Table 2** to summarize the functions of each region in the autonomic peripheral nervous system. K/U C

Table 2 Autonomic PNS

Region	Function
parasympathetic actions in the brain	
parasympathetic actions in the lower spinal cord	
sympathetic actions in the section of the spinal cord in the neck	
sympathetic actions in the section of the spinal cord in the region of the ribs	
sympathetic actions in the lower spinal cord	

MAIN IDEA: Naturally produced painkillers and synthetic painkillers work because they block or reduce the binding of pain neurotransmitters to substantia gelatinosa (SG) receptor cells.

5. Is the body's reaction to pain controlled by the somatic or the autonomic nervous system? Explain. K/U T/I

6. Think of the structure of a chemical synapse. Suggest two ways in which drugs could be used to influence the actions of the synapse. K/U A

7. Studies have suggested that exercise can be as effective in treating depression as antidepressant medications. Why does this make sense? T/I K/U

The Senses

Textbook pp. 542–548

Vocabulary

sensory adaptation

MAIN IDEA: In the visual system, photoreceptors detect light stimuli at particular wavelengths. They convert the stimuli to nerve impulses, which move the information via the optic nerve to the visual centres in the CNS. Hair cells in each ear sense sound and respond by triggering action potentials, sending signals via the auditory nerve to the thalamus and then to the brain's temporal lobe. Chemoreceptors for taste have receptors in taste buds that relay signals to the thalamus and then to gustatory (taste) centres, such as those in the cerebral cortex. Chemoreceptors for smell make direct connections with interneurons in the brain, rather than using afferent neurons as a conduit. Mechanoreceptors for touch and pressure are embedded in the skin and other surface tissues.

1. Indicate which type of receptor(s) will respond to each type of stimulus. **K/U** **A**

    (a) you lean against a wall

    (b) you look at a photograph

    (c) you taste a fruit you like

    (d) a bell rings

    (e) you step outside to see if you need a coat

    (f) you cut your finger

    (g) you walk past a bakery

2. Label **Figure 1** to show the parts of the eye. **K/U** **C**

STUDY TIP

Make Connections
As you perform daily activities, such as walking from one class to another, or eating dinner, think about what types of receptors are working in your nervous system. Where are neurons carrying sensory input? Where are motor and autonomic neurons carrying instructions?

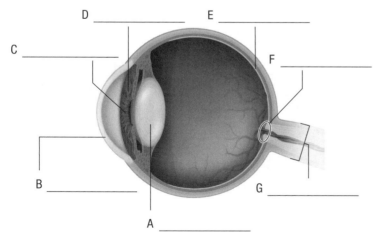

D _____   E _____

C _____

F _____

B _____

G _____

A _____

Figure 1

3. Label **Figure 2** to show the parts of Eustachian tube in the ear. Add the numbers 1 through 6 to show the order in wich these parts become involved in processing sound. (Not every part will have a number, and some will share a number.) K/U C

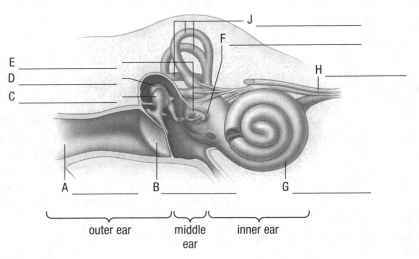

outer ear   middle ear   inner ear

Figure 2

4. Complete **Table 1** to compare how the body processes taste, smell, and touch. K/U T/I C

Table 1 Taste, Smell, and Touch Sensors

	Taste	Smell	Touch
Location of sensors			
Description of sensors			
How messages are conveyed			

5. (a) What sense do most animals have other than sight, hearing, taste, smell, and touch?

(b) Where are the sensors for this sense located? K/U

MAIN IDEA: Some sensory systems become less reactive to a stimulus if it continues at a constant level. This reduction is called sensory adaptation. When the body is subjected to potentially damaging internal and external conditions, nociceptors (pain receptor) detect these damaging stimuli and send a message to the brain that is interpreted as pain.

6. Describe an everyday example of a sensory system becoming less reactive to a continued stimulus. A

7. To what degree do pain receptors become less reactive to a continued stimulus. Why might this be? K/U T/I

MAIN IDEA: A sensory processing disorder is a neurological disorder that causes difficulties in processing information received from sensory receptors. Stimuli are received normally but are perceived or interpreted abnormally.

8. Describe an example of a sensory disorder with a physical cause. K/U

9. Describe common symptoms of sensory processing disorders. K/U

The Body and Stress

Textbook pp. 549–553

> **Vocabulary**
>
> renin-angiotensin-aldosterone pathway

MAIN IDEA: Stress is the body's response to stimuli, or stressors, that cause a disruption in homeostasis. The response is an attempt to restore homeostasis. Stress can be caused by a range of factors. Physical stress, such as exercising, can also cause a stress response. Different individuals may respond differently to the same stress.

1. (a) Define "stress".

   (b) What are the risks of prolonged stress? K/U

2. Describe an example of each type of stress. K/U A
   (a) positive stress

   (b) negative physical stress

   (d) short-term emotional stress

   (e) long-term psychological stress

MAIN IDEA: Symptoms of stress can include accelerated heart rate, sweaty hands, an upset stomach, and rapid breathing. Long-term exposure to stress has been associated with many diseases and negative health effects.

3. Describe a few ways you deal with the stress that you encounter in your life. K/U A

STUDY **TIP**

Controlling Stress
Writing a test or exam can be a cause of stress. However, making a conscious effort to reverse symptoms of stress, for example deliberately breathing slowly and keeping your mind from racing around, can help reduce stress and help you focus on the task at hand.

4. Describe an example of a severe allergic reaction and explain how it produces extreme stress, or shock, in the body. K/U

5. (a) Prostaglandins are part of a stress response. What role do they play?

   (b) How do pain relievers such as acetylsalicylic acid (ASA) work? K/U

MAIN IDEA: The endocrine, nervous, and excretory systems are all involved in the stress response. The endocrine system secretes hormones, such as epinephrine and cortisol. The nervous system responds to brief stressors and also stimulates the endocrine system. The excretory system regulates the volume of fluid in the body and maintains or increases blood pressure during an emergency.

6. (a) How does stress affect hormones in the body?

   (b) How does stress affect the nervous system? K/U

7. Complete the flow chart to show how the body responds to short-term and long-term stress. K/U T/I C

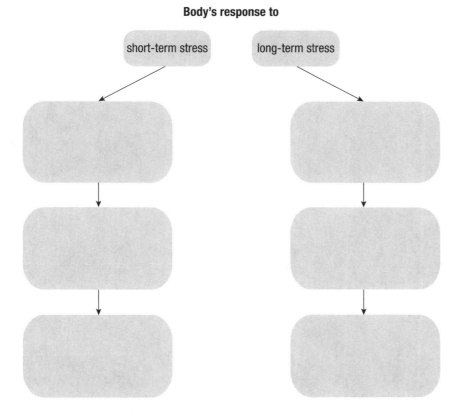

Body's response to

short-term stress   long-term stress

The Nervous System

Complete the flow chart to show the stimulus processed by the brain or the spinal cord and the response or sense that results from the stimulus.

External Stimulus   **Response/Sense**

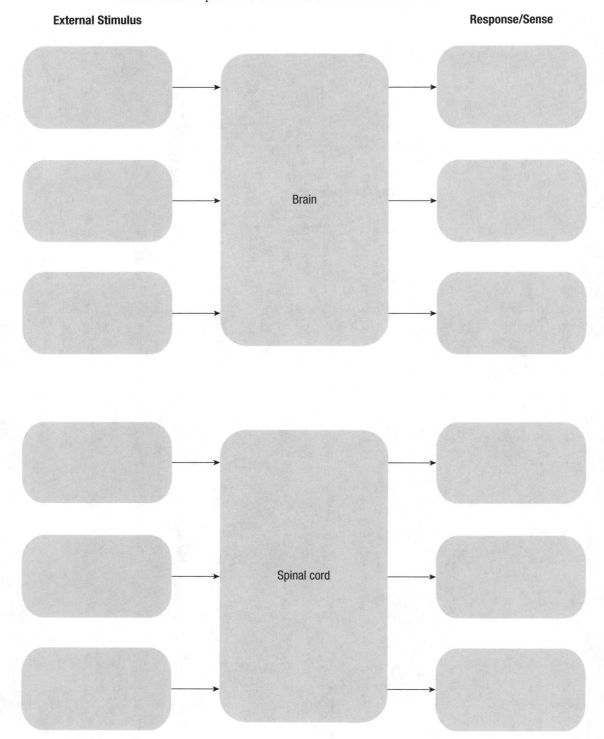

1. Integration of simple responses to certain stimuli, such as the knee-jerk response, is accomplished by which region? (11.1) K/U
   - (a) cerebellum
   - (b) hypothalamus
   - (c) corpus callosum
   - (d) spinal cord

2. Exocytosis is used by the synaptic vesicles to remove their contents at which location? (11.2) K/U
   - (a) presynaptic membrane
   - (b) axon hillock
   - (c) nodes of Ranvier
   - (d) postsynaptic membrane

3. The coordination of motor activities in mammals is carried out by which region in the brain? (11.3) K/U
   - (a) pons
   - (b) cerebellum
   - (c) cerebrum
   - (d) medulla

4. Parasympathetic stimulation would result in which response? (11.4) K/U
   - (a) decreased blood flow in skin
   - (b) pupil dilation
   - (c) increased heart rate
   - (d) decreased activity of digestive tract

5. Indicate whether each statement is true or false. If you think a statement is false, rewrite it to make it true. K/U
   - (a) Electrochemical messages are carried by the movement of ions through the nerve membrane. (11.2)

   - (b) When the nerve cell is excited, it becomes more permeable to potassium ions than sodium ions. (11.2)

   - (c) When an increase in body temperature is detected by sensors in the brain, it sends a nerve message to the hypothalamus. (11.5)

6. Compare and contrast the main functions of the autonomic division of the nervous system and the somatic division of the nervous system (11.4) K/U T/I

7. List three factors that determine an action potential's rate of propagation. (11.2) K/U

8. Which two areas of the brain control respiration? (11.3) K/U

9. A neuron generates an action potential. Describe the concentration of K^+. (11.2) K/U

K/U   Knowledge/Understanding
T/I   Thinking/Investigation
C   Communication
A   Application

10. List four functions performed by the synapses. (11.2) K/U

11. Which part of the neuron receives sensory information? (11.1) K/U

12. Where are interneurons most commonly located? (11.1) K/U

13. You hold the bulb of a thermometer in your right hand and plunge your left hand into ice water. After a few minutes, the temperature on the thermometer decreases. (11.4) K/U T/I C
    (a) Explain why this response occurs.

    (b) How can this be considered an example of homeostasis?

14. During a physical examination, a doctor will usually hit a patient's knee on one side with a small hammer. Instantly the leg jerks upward. (11.1) K/U A
    (a) What is happening in the patient's nervous system?

    (b) What the doctor is testing?

15. People who get inner ear infections often experience dizziness. Explain why this is so given what you know about the structure of the ear. (11.5) K/U A

16. The actor Christopher Reeve fractured his spine in an accident and became paralyzed. Why are people who receive a spinal fracture usually unlikely to recover from the injury? (11.3) K/U T/I A

17. Given what you know about the structure of the ear, explain why competitive high-divers wear earplugs. (11.5) K/U T/I A

K/U Knowledge/Understanding
T/I Thinking/Investigation
C Communication
A Application

1. The sodium pump operates in which part of the nephron? (9.5) K/U
   (a) Bowman's capsule
   (b) collecting tubule
   (c) proximal convoluted tubule
   (d) Loop of Henle

2. In a research laboratory, an anaesthetized mouse has a fine tube inserted into one of its ureters. The number of drops of urine excreted from the fine tube increases dramatically when a small amount of concentrated glucose solution is injected into a vein. Which statement best explains this phenomenon? (9.4) K/U T/I
   (a) Glucose in concentrated solution is isotonic to the extracellular fluid.
   (b) A great increase in the amount of plasma increases the rate of formation of urine.
   (c) The amount of glucose in the urine increases if the glucose content of the diet or blood increases.
   (d) Glucose affects osmosis, one of the mechanisms involved in the formation of urine.

3. Where are excess hydrogen ions removed from the body? (11.2) K/U
   (a) in the distal tubules after a reaction with glucose
   (b) in the distal tubules after a reaction with urea
   (c) in the nephron during a reaction with aldosterone
   (d) in the lungs after reaction with bicarbonate ions

4. Indicate whether each statement is true or false. If you think a statement is false, rewrite it to make it true. K/U
   (a) Plasma proteins, erythrocytes, and platelets are transferred to the Bowman's capsule. (9.5)

   (b) Calcitonin and parathyroid hormone regulate calcium levels in the blood. (10.1)

   (c) Large levels of testosterone in the blood deactivate the hypothalamus, which in turn stops the production of luteinizing hormone (LH). (10.7)

   (d) There are more nerve networks leading to the legs and arms than to the thumb and fingers. (11.1)

5. In times of stress, the adrenal gland promotes the synthesis of glucose from non-carbohydrate substrates by secreting which hormone? (11.4) K/U

6. (a) In the female reproductive cycle, when are LH levels the highest?
   _____

   (b) What hormone activity occurs at puberty? _____

   (c) What hormone activity causes menstruation? _____

   (d) The growing follicle secretes which hormone? _____ (10.7) K/U

7. **Table 1** shows the blood test results for four renal patients and the expected results for a healthy person. (9.5) K/U T/I

Table 1 Renal Patient Blood Test Results

	Urea	Uric acid	Glucose	Amino acid	Proteins
Normal Results	0.030	0.004	0.10	0.05	8.00
Mrs. Fernandez	0.030	0.004	0.50	0.05	8.00
Mr. Morgan	0.030	0.005	1.70	0.05	8.00
Mr. Capelli	0.030	0.050	0.10	0.05	8.00
Ms Wong	0.030	0.004	0.10	0.06	4.00

(a) Which patient has probably just eaten some sugar? Explain.

(b) Which patient is most likely experiencing capsular failure? Explain.

(c) Which patient has probably eaten a meal with a high protein content? Explain.

8. Why can a larger volume of fluid move across the glomerular membrane than across the membranes of other body capillaries? (9.5) K/U

9. Body temperature in endotherms is generally maintained within a narrow range but this is not always the case. For example, a diet high in protein can increase metabolism, resulting in a higher body temperature. Describe three other situations where body temperature is higher or lower than the norm. Briefly explain the cause and the possible consequences of each situation. (9.3) K/U T/I A

10. For any given steroid hormone, there are DNA gene sequences for the hormone, for the steroid hormone receptor and for the steroid hormone response element. Discuss how this leads to confusion when biotechnology researchers announce they have found the gene for a specific genetic disorder involving a steroid. (10.1) K/U T/I A

11. What is the function of acetylcholine in humans? (11.2) K/U

Population Dynamics

Chapter 12: Natural Population Dynamics

Populations of organisms are dynamic and ever-changing. They are affected by natural factors such as disease and erosion. They are also affected by human activities, such as the introduction of species into a new habitat.

Biologists use sampling and tracking techniques to study factors that can help them monitor the health of natural populations. The distribution of a species describes where it lives and how widespread it is. Within its range, a population inhabits a specific habitat, defined by a set of specific biotic and abiotic conditions.

The size of a population changes with time, directly influenced by birth rates, death rates, immigration and emigration. Scientists track information about these factors on life tables and survivorship curves, and analyze their effects using models such as the exponential growth model, the geometric growth model, and the logistic growth model. Each model has a particular function. The exponential and geometric growth models describe population growth when resources are assumed to be unlimited. Carrying capacity is the upper limit to the number of people an environment can support. The logistic growth model assumes that the population growth rate is negative when the population size exceeds its carrying capacity. The growth of populations is influenced by competition, predation and herbivory, symbiotic relationships such as parasitism, disease, crowding, changes to habitat quality, and other disturbances.

A population's density gives a sense of how many individuals live in a specific area. Large species generally have a small population density, whereas smaller species often have a much larger population density.

BIG IDEAS

- Population growth follows predictable patterns.

- The increased consumption of resources and production of waste associated with population growth result in specific stresses that can affect Earth's sustainability.

- Technological developments can contribute to or help offset the ecological footprint associated with population growth and the consumption of natural resources.

Chapter 13: Human Population Dynamics

Earth's human population is affected by the same factors as the populations of other species. However, by learning to change our environment through developing agriculture and other technologies, our population has grown exponentially and now threatens to exceed Earth's carrying capacity.

The human population started out growing slowly as people domesticated plants and animals to feed their families. Human population growth sped up when villages and towns formed to share resources and knowledge. The development of medical vaccines, industrialized agriculture, and the ability to extract energy from fossil fuels allowed the human population to grow even more quickly.

This rapid growth has come at a high cost. With a current human population of over 7 billion, we are now using more resources each year than Earth can create. Soil resources are being depleted, air and water resources are being degraded, and global biodiversity is decreasing. The ecological footprint is a measure of all the biological resources we use and the carbon dioxide that is produced over a year. It can be calculated for a person, a community, or a country. Individuals, governments, and industries have begun to research and develop more sustainable ways of providing food, heating homes, and transporting people and goods, to reduce our ecological footprints. These efforts are essential if we want to change the path we are on.

Population Characteristics

Textbook pp. 584–592

Vocabulary

population ecology	habitat	crude density	quadrat
geographic range	population size (N_t)	ecological density	mark-recapture method
	population density (D)	dispersion	

MAIN IDEA: Biologists use measurements, such as population size and population density, to describe and monitor populations. These measurements also help biologists manage species.

1. (a) Describe two examples of a range.

   (b) Describe two examples of a habitat. K/U

2. The population of an introduced plant species in a conservation area doubles every ten years. K/U T/I A
   (a) What population measurement is described above?

   (b) What could wildlife biologists learn from this data? How could they use this information to manage this plant species and others in the area?

3. Name two animals that are likely to have a low population density. Why will their population density be low? K/U T/I

MAIN IDEA: Populations in a given geographical range show one of three dispersion patterns: clumped, uniform, or random.

4. Name and describe the dispersion patterns shown in **Figures 1, 2**, and **3**. Provide an example of a species that often demonstrates each dispersion pattern. K/U T/I C

   (a)

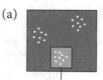

Figure 1

(b)

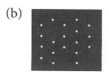

Figure 2

(c)

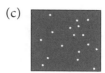

Figure 3

5. Complete the following description of changing animal dispersions. K/U

The _____ of an animal population often varies over time. For example, in wet seasons, when _____ is widely available, tropical birds and mammals may show _____ dispersion, spreading over a large area. In dry seasons, the same animals may show _____ dispersion, grouping together in areas where _____ and _____ can be found.

MAIN IDEA: Biologists use quadrat sampling and mark-recapture sampling to estimate population size and density. Satellite and other technology can be used to track animals that migrate or move over long distances.

6. List three indirect indicators that biologists can use to estimate population size when it is difficult to count the individuals in a population. K/U

7. (a) What factor determines the size of quadrat a biologist will use to estimate population size?

(b) What factor determines the location of the quadrat used to estimate population size? K/U

8. Use a flow chart to describe the four steps used in mark-recapture sampling. K/U C

9. How can tracking a population help biologists to manage the population? T/I

MAIN IDEA: Ethical issues and concerns need to be considered when studying and monitoring wildlife populations.

10. List three potential positive results of tracking and monitoring wild populations. T/I

11. List two potential negative results of tracking and monitoring wild populations. T/I

Demography

Textbook pp. 593–599

Vocabulary

demography	emigration	age-specific mortality	fecundity
natality	life table	age-specific survivorship	generation time
mortality	cohort	survivorship curve	sex ratio
immigration			

MAIN IDEA: Populations are dynamic and change based on many factors, including birth and death rates, immigration, emigration, fecundity, and generation time.

1. Complete the following equation to show how four factors affect population change. K/U

   population change =

   (_____ + _____) − (_____ + _____)

2. (a) Suggest two factors that could increase the birth rate in a population.

   (b) Suggest two factors that could increase the death rate in a population. K/U A

3. Complete the following paragraph to describe how environmental conditions can affect fecundity. K/U

   When food is _____ and the _____ is optimal, fecundity tends to _____. When food is _____ or there is little _____, fecundity tends to _____.

4. Why is it important for population biologists to study age-specific fecundity in a species? Use an example in your answer. A

MAIN IDEA: Life tables are used to describe and understand the population dynamics of a species. Survivorship curves depict survival in a population at different ages and can be constructed for a given cohort based on the data in a life table.

5. Circle the types of information would you find on a life table. K/U
   (a) number of individuals that died in each age interval
   (b) number of individuals that survived at each age interval
   (c) age at which an individual died
   (d) number of offspring an individual produced
   (e) average number of offspring at each age interval
   (f) age at which an individual produced the most offspring

6. What is the difference between age-specific mortality and age-specific survivorship? **K/U**

7. **Figure 1** shows the survivorship rate for the bluegrass plant. What is the probability a bluegrass plant will be alive at 11 months but not at 15 months? **T/I** **A**

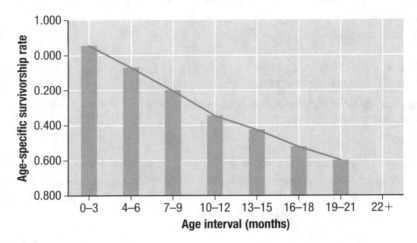

Figure 1

8. How can survivorship curves help a biologist monitor a population? **T/I**

MAIN IDEA: There is an inverse relationship between fecundity and parental care. In general, the higher the fecundity of a species, the lower the parental care is.

STUDY TIP

Make a Sketch
Sketch a quick graph to help you remember relationships such as this one.

9. Draw a graph to illustrate the relationship between fecundity and the amount of parental care a species provides. **K/U** **C**

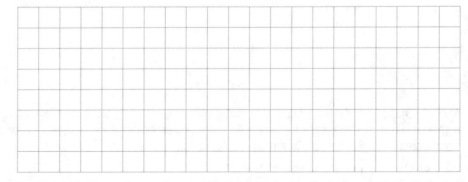

10. Describe the fecundity and amount of parental care for humans. Does it fit the pattern? Why or why not? **T/I** **A**

12.3
Changes in Population Size over Time: Modelling Population Growth

Textbook pp. 600–609

Vocabulary

population dynamics

exponential model of population growth

per capita growth rate (*r*)

zero population growth (ZPG)

carrying capacity (*K*)

logistic model of population growth

sigmoid curve (logistic)

MAIN IDEA: Mathematical models and graphs help ecologists predict and monitor trends in populations.

1. Describe an example of a population whose growth is monitored. How are the results of the monitoring used? K/U T/I

2. The growth rate of a population is −3 %. What does this mean? K/U T/I

3. In a population of 100 foxes, 12 are born and 9 die in a given year. T/I A
   (a) Calculate the per capita birth rate.

   (b) Calculate the per capita death rate.

4. Why are human birth rates measured per year and fruit fly birth rates measured per day? T/I

> **STUDY TIP**
>
> **Formulas**
> To help ensure you are using the correct formula for a calculation, substitute simple numbers into the formula, calculate in your head (if possible), and check that the answer is reasonable.

MAIN IDEA: Exponential growth and geometric growth models describe population growth when resources are assumed to be unlimited.

5. A population of bacteria grows exponentially. In the first generation there are two cells. How many cells are there in the sixth generation? A

6. Express the equation below in words. K/U C

$$\frac{dN}{dt} = rN$$

7. (a) What type of growth is shown on the graph in **Figure 1** below?

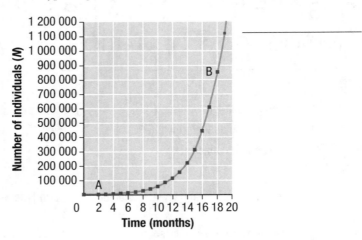

_____

Figure 1

(b) Explain how the population size is changing at point A and at point B. Why is the population size changing as it is? K/U T/I C

8. A population has a growth rate of 9 % per year. What is its doubling time? T/I A

9. (a) What type of growth is shown on the graph in **Figure 2** below?

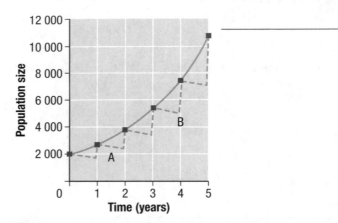

_____

Figure 2

(b) Explain how the population size is changing at point A and at point B. Why is the population size changing as it is? K/U T/I C

MAIN IDEA: There is an upper limit to the number of individuals that most environments can support. This upper limit is known as the carrying capacity of the population. The logistic growth model assumes that the population growth rate cannot be positive when the population size exceeds its carrying capacity.

10. Draw a graph showing the exponential growth of a population and the change in growth rate once the population's carrying capacity is reached. Label the carrying capacity on your graph. K/U C

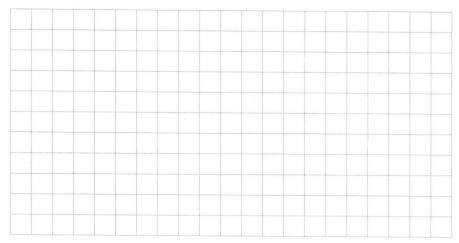

11. Describe two factors that can affect the carrying capacity of a population. K/U

12. The logistic model of population growth attempts to reflect the factors that affect growth in the real world. It describes growth that slows as the carrying capacity is reached. Complete this paragraph to explain how a population's growth rate will change as the population size approaches the carrying capacity. K/U

If a population is very small (N much smaller than _____), _____ of resources are available and therefore the value of $\frac{(K - N)}{K}$ is close to _____.

In this case, the per capita growth rate approaches the _____ possible. If a population is very large (N close to _____), _____ resources are available. The value of $\frac{(K - N)}{K}$ is _____, and the per capita growth rate is very _____.

13. (a) List the assumptions that the logistic model of growth makes.

    (b) Since few populations in the real world meet these assumptions, does this mean that the logistic model of growth is invalid? Explain. K/U T/I A

Factors that Affect Population Growth

Textbook pp. 610–615

> **Vocabulary**
>
> limiting factor
>
> density-dependent factor
>
> density-independent factor
>
> competition
>
> interspecific competition
>
> intraspecific competition
>
> predation
>
> Allee affect
>
> minimum viable
>   population size

MAIN IDEA: Populations are dynamic. The growth of a population is limited by the presence or absence of factors that are necessary for survival.

1. (a) List two biotic factors that can limit the growth of a population.

   (b) List two biotic factors that can accelerate the growth of a population. K/U

2. (a) List two abiotic factors that can limit the growth of a population.

   (b) List two abotic factors that can accelerate the growth of a population. K/U

MAIN IDEA: Density-dependent factors limit the growth of a population and are dependent on population density.

3. Complete the following sentence. K/U

   As the _____ of a population increases, the effects of most density-dependent factors _____.

4. Describe four types of density-dependent factors. Use an example to show how each one is density-dependent. K/U T/I

5. Do the effects of all density-dependent factors increase as the density of a population increases? Explain. K/U T/I

6. How have some plants overcome the Allee effect and reproduce even in low population densities? K/U

MAIN IDEA: Density-independent factors limit the growth of a population regardless of population density.

7. Complete the following sentence. K/U

   As the _____ of a population increases, the effects of most density-independent factors _____.

8. (a) List four examples of natural disturbances that are density-independent factors.

   (b) What disturbance caused by humans is acting as a density-independent factor to limit growth of many natural populations? K/U

9. Forest fires in northern Ontario are part of a feedback loop that involves deforestation and climate change. Draw a flow chart to illustrate this positive feedback loop. T/I C

STUDY **TIP**

Flow Charts
Flow charts can be very useful to illustrate the effects of biotic and abiotic relationships in the study of population dynamics.

Interactions between Individuals

Vocabulary			
coevolution	parasitism	interference competition	realized niche
herbivory	commensalism	exploitative competition	resource partitioning
mutualism	mimicry	fundamental niche	

MAIN IDEA: Many different kinds of interactions, which occur both among and between species, affect population growth. Interspecific interactions can be predatory, herbivorous, competitive, mutualistic, commensal or parasitic.

1. Name the type(s) of interaction for each relationship. **K/U**
   (a) both interacting populations gain _____
   (b) both interacting populations lose _____
   (c) one of the interacting populations is unaffected _____
   (d) one of the interacting populations gains and one loses

   _____

2. Mutualism, commensalism, and parasitism are all types of symbiosis or a particularly close association between two species. What type of symbiosis is described in each situation? **A**
   (a) Black bears eat fruit and deposit the seeds in their fecal matter.

   (b) Kidney worms live in, and consume, the right kidney of minks.

   (c) Cattle egrets follow elephants around and eat the insects flushed from the grasses.

   (d) Mistletoe attaches to a tree and takes water and nutrients from it.

   (e) Humans keep cats and dogs as pets.

MAIN IDEA: Predator–prey interactions are affected by many factors. Both the predator and the prey coevolve to enhance their survival.

3. What is the main difference between predation and herbivory? **K/U**

4. Describe two adaptations predators have evolved that help them obtain food. **K/U**

5. Food availability often affects the food sources animals will choose. Based on this, complete each of the following sentences. **K/U**
   (a) When food is abundant _____

   _____

   (b) When food is scarce _____

   _____

6. Many species that are prey have evolved defense mechanisms. Describe five types of defence mechanisms. [K/U]

7. **Figure 1** shows the population of a predator and its prey over time. [K/U] [T/I]

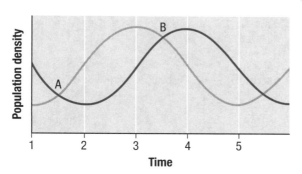

Figure 1

STUDY TIP

Using Examples
Use an example from the real world, for example the relationship between lynxes and hares, to help you understand and remember each type of interaction between individuals.

(a) Which line shows the predator population? _____

(b) Describe what is happening at point A and point B.

MAIN IDEA: Competition among ecologically similar species is a factor that affects their population growth.

8. What is the difference between interference competition and exploitative competition? [K/U]

9. **Figure 2** shows the size of two populations that compete for resources over time. Why does the size of one population decrease to a much lower level than the size of the other? [T/I]

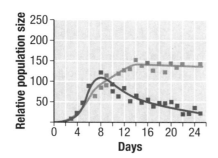

Figure 2

10. **Figure 3** shows the root systems of three plants that live in the same place.
K/U T/I

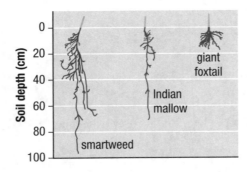

Figure 3

(a) How are these plants partitioning the resources available in their habitat?

(b) How could these three plants occupying the same area have led to the evolution of different characteristics?

MAIN IDEA: Loss of a species, invasion of a non-native species, and human interference can disrupt the stability of an ecosystem.

11. Suppose wolves were completely removed from Ontario. Describe what would probably happen to the size of each of the following populations as a direct result of wolf removal. T/I A

(a) deer

(b) vegetation eaten by deer

(c) other animals that eat the same vegetation

(d) predators of the animals that eat the same vegetation as deer

12. A healthy ecosystem is a diverse ecosystem. What happens to ecosystem diversity when a non-native species is introduced and outcompetes native species? T/I

Natural Population Dynamics

A: Demography Refer to the following web, and your notes about each item in it, to review how various tools and techniques are used to measure population characteristics.

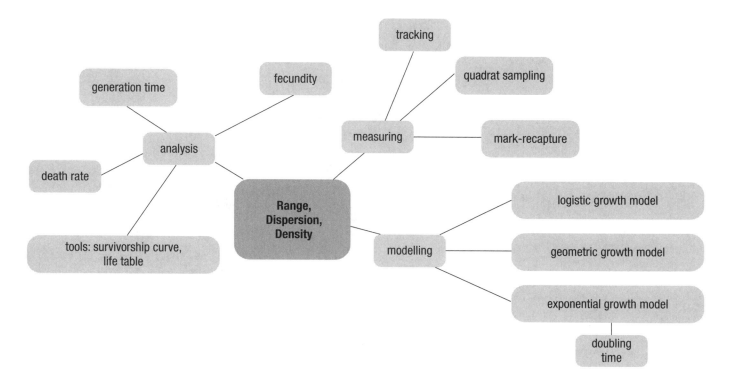

B: Population Dynamics The following graphic organizer shows factors that can lead to population increases and factors that can lead to population decreases. How does each factor exert its effect? Which factors are density dependent?

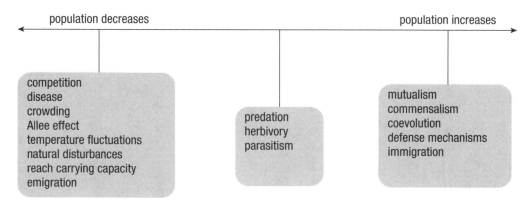

K/U   Knowledge/Understanding
T/I   Thinking/Investigation
C   Communication
A   Application

1. What technique can biologists use to learn about a population's range, distribution, population density, and migration routes? (12.1) K/U
   (a) the logistical growth model
   (b) mark-recapture sampling
   (c) animal tracking
   (d) life tables

2. Identify the model of population growth that produces an S-shaped graph, leveling off near the carrying capacity. (12.3) K/U
   (a) carrying capacity model
   (b) logistic growth model
   (c) geometric growth model
   (d) exponential growth model

3. Indicate whether each statement is true or false. If you think a statement is false, rewrite it to make it true. K/U
   (a) Low population density can make it more difficult to find a mate, causing individuals in the species to breed with individuals of other species. (12.4)

   (b) Three factors that affect the fecundity of a species are environment, for example the amount of food available; age of sexual maturity; and birth rate. (12.2)

4. What ratio can be used to estimate the population sizes using the mark-recapture method of sampling? (12.1) A

5. Female snapping turtles lay up to 50 eggs in a sandy spot. Up to 90 % of snapping turtle nests are destroyed by predators and the eggs eaten. Many of the young turtles that do hatch are also eaten. Only 1 in approximately 1400 eggs produces a hatchling that survives to adulthood. Once a snapping turtle is more than approximately 9 cm long, it has no natural predators. Sketch a survivorship curve for snapping turtles. (12.2) C A

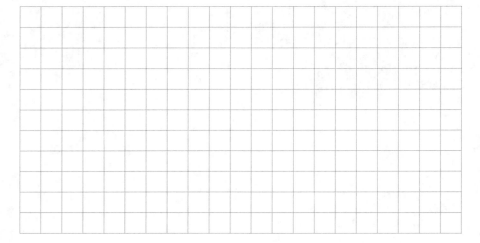

6. Complete the equation to show how population growth rate can be calculated. (12.3) K/U C

$$\frac{(\rule{3cm}{0.4pt}) - (\rule{3cm}{0.4pt})}{(\rule{4cm}{0.4pt})} \times 100\ \%$$

7. Describe two examples of density-dependent factors and density-independent factors that affect population growth. (12.4) K/U

8. There are two populations of a certain type of owl in Ontario's forests. One is a relatively dense population and the other is not. Which of the following factors would you expect to affect the growth of both owl populations equally? Why? T/I
   - a new parasite
   - a forest fire

9. Complete this description of ecological niches. (12.5) K/U
   A plant population's niche includes _____, _____, and _____. An animal population's niche includes_____, _____, and _____. Often, when several species coexist in one area, they occupy different _____.

10. Explain the differences between the three types of symbiosis. Use examples in your explanation. (12.5) K/U C

11. List three ways humans interfere with ecosystem relationships. (12.5) K/U

Human Population: Past and Present

Vocabulary

ecological footprint	Industrial Revolution	Aboriginal peoples	replacement rate
pathogen	vaccine	demographic transition model	
epidemic	population pyramid		

MAIN IDEA: Human population growth changes over time and varies significantly by region. Agricultural and industrial revolutions have led to surges in the human population. Advancements in science, technology, and medicine have led to decreases in the mortality rate.

1. Why did agriculture develop more quickly in some parts of the world than in others? K/U

2. Draw a flow chart to show how the domestication of plants and animals led to growth of the human population. T/I C

3. What three factors contributed to epidemics among Aboriginal peoples after Europeans arrived in North America? K/U

4. Fill in **Table 1** to describe the social impact and the environmental impact of each scientific and technological breakthrough. K/U T/I C

Table 1 Impact of Human Breakthroughs

Breakthrough	Social impact	Environmental impact
vaccines		
antibiotics		
water treatment		
steam engine		
fertilizers		

MAIN IDEA: Age pyramids represent age distributions across a population.

5. Why do population pyramids show numbers of males on one side and numbers of females on the other side? [T/I]

6. **Figure 1** shows an age pyramid for the population of the United States in 2000. [T/I] [A]

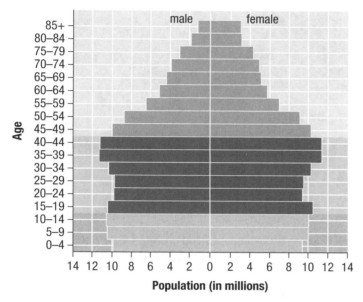

Figure 1

(a) Describe the age distribution, based on the pyramid.

(b) Predict the age distribution in the United States in 2030. Include evidence from the age pyramid.

MAIN IDEA: Demographics for the Aboriginal population in Canada suggest that there may be a population increase in the next decade, due to a large number of young people.

7. **Table 2** shows the median age of four Aboriginal groups in Canada. Which group would you expect to have an age pyramid with the widest base? Why? [T/I]

Table 2 Median Age of Aboriginal Groups

	First Nations	**Métis**	**Inuit**
Median age	24.9	29.5	21.5

8. **Figure 2** shows a population pyramid for Canada's Aboriginal identity population. Who might be interested in analyzing this graph? How might the analysis be helpful to them? T/I A

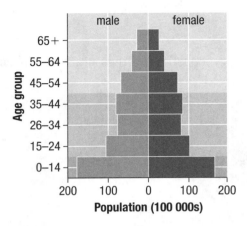

Figure 2

MAIN IDEA: The relationship between population growth and economic development in many countries can be represented by the demographic transition model.

9. Complete the paragraph to describe the changes in birth rate and death rate according to the demographic transition model. K/U

   During a country's pre-industrial stage, _____ and _____ rates are _____ and the population grows slowly. During the transitional stage, food production _____, health _____, and the population grows _____. By the industrial stage, the cost of supporting a large family causes the birth rate to _____, which causes population growth to _____. Eventually, in the post-industrial stage, the birth rate becomes lower than the _____, and population size _____.

10. (a) According to the demographic transition model, why might some developing countries stay in the transitional stage and maintain a high rate of population growth?

    (b) What does the demographic transitional model suggest about possible ways to control global human population growth? K/U T/I

11. Population growth slows significantly if many women decide to wait a few years before they have their first child. Why is this more likely to happen in an industrial or post-industrial society? T/I

Implications of Human Population Growth

Textbook pp. 653–666

Vocabulary

malnutrition	energy pyramid	sustainable agriculture	bycatch
industrialized agriculture	trophic level	(low-input agriculture)	aquaculture
traditional agriculture	salinization	organic agriculture	

MAIN IDEA: The move from rural areas to urban areas had advantages for human populations, but it also required the development of more infrastructure and services, such as transportation and sanitation.

1. There are many reasons large numbers of people have moved from rural areas to urban areas. Describe three. K/U

2. Complete the following paragraph to describe some ways urban environments can stress the natural environment. K/U

   Increased demands for _____ and_____

   create _____ and air quality issues. Sending solid waste to

   _____ creates pollution and is an _____

   use of land. Cities and their populations consume large amounts of

   _____, draining _____. To make

   cities sustainable, these issues must be addressed.

MAIN IDEA: The present food supply is adequate to feed all the people in the world, but food production and distribution are unequally distributed worldwide.

3. (a) List two areas in the world that consume less food per day than the minimum amount recommended by the United Nations.

   (b) List two areas in the world that consume more food per day than the minimum amount recommended by the United Nations. K/U

4. Describe five of the main causes of hunger in the world. K/U

MAIN IDEA: Agriculture is necessary to grow our food, but some of our agricultural techniques have a high impact on natural resources. High-input agriculture uses resources such as water and electricity to produce food. Low-input agriculture requires only human and animal labour.

5. What factors contribute to agriculture's ecological footprint? K/U

6. Contrast traditional agriculture and industrialized agriculture. K/U T/I

7. Would you classify aquaculture as a form of agriculture? Why or why not? T/I

MAIN IDEA: Low-impact diets require less energy and reduce our ecological footprint.

8. The energy pyramid in **Figure 1** shows the energy transfer from plant producers to livestock and then to humans. The energy available in the plants is 500 kJ. Add labels to show the amount of energy available at each step in the pyramid. C

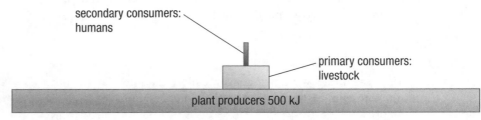

Figure 1

9. What are three actions we can take to lower the ecological impact of our diets? K/U A

MAIN IDEA: Soil quality is threatened in many areas, leading to erosion and nutrient loss.

10. (a) What human activities cause erosion by destroying plant cover?

    (b) How can humans prevent erosion? K/U

11. Describe the positive and negative effects of irrigation on soil. K/U

12. What are two techniques farmers can use to restore lost nutrients to soil? K/U

MAIN IDEA: Water is one of our most precious resources, yet it is not well protected. Water pollution comes from many sources, including agriculture, industry, and human waste.

13. Draw a flow chart to show how the world's water supply is continuously collected, purified, and recycled in the hydrologic cycle. T/I C

14. (a) Describe five forms of water pollution.

    (b) Add arrows to your flow chart in question 13 to show where each form of pollution enters the hydrologic cycle. K/U C

MAIN IDEA: Air pollution has far-reaching effects, most significantly air quality and climate change.

15. What causes air pollution? Include examples. K/U

LEARNING TIP

Diagrams
The image of the hydrologic cycle (water cycle) can help you remember how air and soil pollution can affect water quality.

16. How can air pollution affect human health? K/U

Textbook pp. 667–668

Feeding a Growing Population

MAIN IDEA: Hunger is a complex issue. A number of Canadian organizations exist to help reduce hunger around the world. By evaluating the effectiveness of these organizations, they can become more productive.

1. What factors affect hunger around the world? K/U

2. List four Canadian organizations that are geared toward increasing global food production. K/U

STUDY TIP

Evaluation

To help focus your evaluation, establish criteria before you begin. Decide what you would expect to see in an organization that does effective work. Be prepared to revise your criteria, though, as you learn more about what is actually being done.

3. What qualities do you think identify an effective agency geared to reducing hunger? T/I

4. In your opinion, should Canadian organizations geared to reducing hunger around the world be funded by governments or by public donations? Why? T/I C

Human Population: The Future

Vocabulary

ecological deficit   biocapacity

Textbook pp. 669–674

MAIN IDEA: Biocapacity is the capacity of an area to provide biological resources and absorb wastes. The effects of the consumption of an ever-increasing human population are overburdening Earth's natural resources.

1. Describe two concerns that are causing many people to reassess their use of natural resources. K/U

2. (a) What three factors can decrease the biocapacity of land?

   (b) What two factors can increase the biocapacity of land? K/U

3. The human population is increasing rapidly. Describe four ways that it is overburdening Earth's natural resources. K/U

4. What goals does the United Nations believe could help control human population growth? K/U

> **STUDY TIP**
>
> **Analogies**
> You can think of biocapacity as a bank account and our use of resources as withdrawals from that account. What happens if you regularly withdraw more money from the account than is deposited? Concrete analogies like this can help you remember many biological concepts.

MAIN IDEA: The ecological footprint measures all the biological materials that are consumed and the carbon dioxide emissions that are released over the period of a year. It can be calculated for an individual, a community, or a country.

5. (a) Residents of which Canadian province have the largest biological footprint?

   (b) Why do you think this may be? T/I

---

6. Why could we be heading for an ecological deficit? K/U

7. What are some consequences of living in an ecological deficit? K/U

MAIN IDEA: Earth's biodiversity is threatened by the demands of the human population. As a global community, we need to safeguard and enhance our biodiversity through conservation and sustainable practices.

8. In **Table 1** below, describe three ways that the demands of a growing human population can decrease biodiversity. Include evidence suggesting that each human activity affects biodiversity. T/I C

Table 1 Ways a Growing Human Population Can Decrease Biodiversity

Ways biodiversity is decreased	Evidence

9. Describe three examples of interventions that are already in place to help reduce the burden our large human population is placing on Earth's environment. K/U

10. What changes could you make to your life immediately to help safeguard biodiversity? A

Biology JOURNAL

The Living Planet Report

MAIN IDEA: *The Living Planet Report* tracks the changing state of Earth's biodiversity and suggests ways that we can move toward positive change. Earth's biodiversity has been decreasing but by changing our ways we can maintain and enhance biodiversity.

1. What two indicators do the World Wildlife Fund, the Zoological Society of London and the Global Footprint Network use to determine the health of the planet? K/U

2. (a) How does Canada's ecological footprint compare to that of other countries?

   (b) Does this result surprise you? Why or why not? K/U T/I

3. What two trends has *The Living Planet Report* revealed? K/U

4. (a) What six strategies does *The Living Planet Report* suggest to move toward positive change?

   (b) Choose two of the suggestions you listed in part (a) and describe three examples of specific actions that support that strategy. K/U T/I

Human Population Dynamics

The factors shown below have resulted in the rapid human population growth. Add examples of each factor involved.

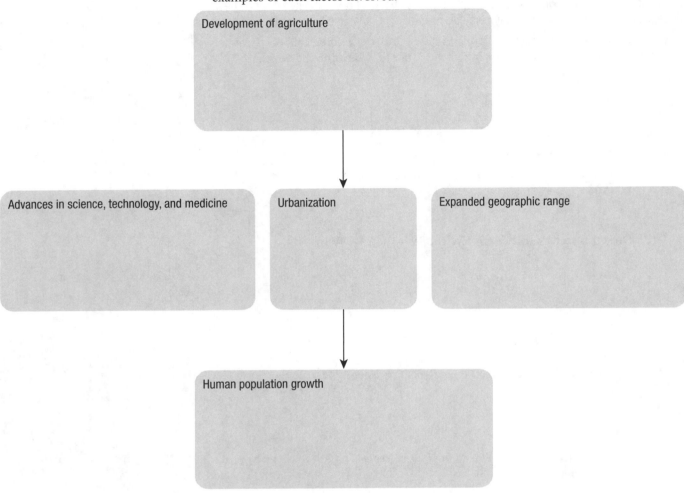

Development of agriculture

Advances in science, technology, and medicine

Urbanization

Expanded geographic range

Human population growth

Complete **Table 1** to summarize what you learned in Chapter 13.

Table 1 Controlling the Effects of Human Growth

Effect of human population growth	Strategy to control effect
industrialized agriculture	
disease epidemics	
soil depletion	
degradation of water and air quality	
reduced biodiversity	
hunger	
ecological deficit	

1. Which population other than humans grew as humans developed agriculture and settled in towns? (13.1) **K/U**
   (a) other primates
   (b) pathogens
   (c) large predators
   (d) herbivores

2. The human population is certain to grow for at least the next 40 years. Why? (13.1) **K/U**
   (a) Currently, children outnumber adults. These children will soon mature and reproduce, causing the population to rise in the near future.
   (b) It will take at least 40 years for all countries to move to a post-industrial stage of development.
   (c) Our logistic growth curve does not show a levelling out until approximately 2060.
   (d) The low birth rate is offset by high rates of immigration.

3. Indicate whether each statement is true or false. If you think the statement is false, rewrite it to make it true. **K/U** **T/I**
   (a) Plantation agriculture is a form of traditional agriculture. (13.2)

   (b) A low-impact diet can include practices such as eating food grown locally. (13.2)

4. Complete this paragraph to describe some recent consequences of the rapidly growing human population. (13.1) **K/U**
   By the middle of the twentieth century, as a result of advancements in
   _____, _____, and _____, the human
   population seemed to be growing without _____. However, some
   consequences of this growth were becoming apparent. These included land
   _____, loss of _____, _____ of wetlands,
   and species _____.

5. There is disagreement among analysts about whether we can increase world food production to feed 7 billion people. (13.2) **K/U**
   (a) What is one reason some analysts believe this is possible?

   (b) What are some reasons other analysts have doubts?

6. What are four key ways that soil can become degraded? (13.2) **K/U**

7. Organic farmers do not use commercial fertilizers. How do they manage soil health? (13.2) T/I

8. What can we do to ensure our water supply continues to by purified by the hydrologic cycle? (13.2) T/I

9. Complete the paragraph to describe some things humans can do to improve air quality. (13.2) K/U

One a large scale, we can clean up _____ emissions and use _____ energy sources. On an individual basis, we can burn less _____ and use less _____ to reduce our global footprint.

10. Why does a rainforest have a higher biocapacity than a desert? (13.4) K/U

11. The demographic transition model describes changes in relative population size as a country passes through four stages of economic development. Sketch the relative population size on the graph in **Figure 1**. (13.1) K/U C

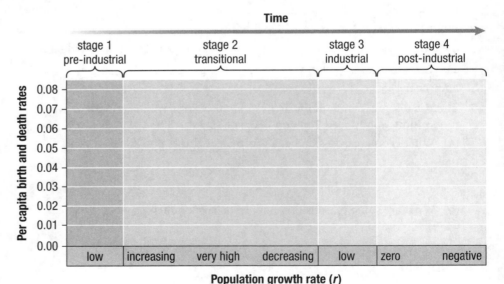

Figure 1

1. Which measurement describes the number of individuals per unit area in the part of a habitat that is actually used? (12.1) K/U
   (a) range
   (b) dispersal
   (c) crude density
   (d) ecological density

2. What is the rate at which humans must reproduce to achieve zero population growth? (13.1) K/U
   (a) zero children per couple
   (b) slightly higher than 1 child per couple
   (c) slightly lower than 2 children per couple
   (d) slightly higher than 2 children per couple

3. Indicate whether each statement is true or false. If you think a statement is false, rewrite it to make it true. K/U
   (a) Symbiosis describes a close ecological association between two species where both species benefit in all cases. (12.5)

   (b) Traditional agriculture is an example of high-input agriculture. (13.2)

4. Describe the relationship between amount of parental care and fecundity. (12.2) K/U

5. (a) Define "carrying capacity."

   (b) How does carrying capacity affect population growth? (12.3) K/U

6. How can resource partitioning help species avoid competition? Give an example. (12.5) T/I A

7. What three grains supply over 50 % of the calories eaten by humans around the world? (13.2) K/U

8. What three developments allowed the human population to grow exponentially? (13.1) K/U

K/U Knowledge/Understanding
T/I Thinking/Investigation
C Communication
A Application

9. Is Earth currently able to support its entire human population? Explain. (13.4) T/I

10. (a) Describe two examples of sustainable agricultural practices.

    (b) Why are some farmers adopting sustainable agricultural techniques? (13.2) K/U T/I

11. What does an ecological footprint measure? (13.4) K/U

12. Sketch a graph to show the pattern described by each model. (12.3) K/U C
    (a) exponential growth   (b) logistic growth

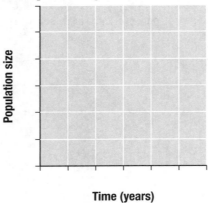
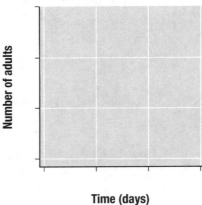

13. Draw a diagram to show how contaminants such as sulfur dioxide can cause water pollution. (13.2) K/U C

14. Suggest economic and environmental advantages and limitations for banning the sale of plastic water bottles. (13.5) K/U T/I C

Answers

These pages include numerical and short answers to chapter section questions, Chapter Questions, and Unit Questions.

Unit 1

1.1, pp. 2–5
11. A, B
13. a

1.2, pp. 6–7
4. Hydrophobic, hydrophilic
5. (a) 0
   (b) 14
   (c) 0
   (d) 14
   (e) 7.4
   (f) 3
   (g) 7

1.3, pp. 8–9
3. no
8. (a) dehydration
   (b) hydrolysis

1.4, pp. 10–12
1. source of energy, building materials, cell communication
4. H_2O
6. polymerization, monomers, dehydration, polymers
8. energy storage, building materials, hormones, vitamins
10. (a) glycerol
    (b) 3 fatty acids
11. (a) hydrophilic head
    (b) polar
    (c) phosphate group
    (d) glycerol
    (e) fatty acid chain
    (f) hydrophobic tail
    (g) non-polar
14. e.g., plants, birds, bees

1.5, pp. 13–15
2. (b) non-polar, uncharged polar, negatively charged polar, positively charged polar
3. R-group, amino acid, peptide, polypeptide, protein
4. (a) secondary structure
   (b) tertiary structure
   (c) primary structure
6. (a) RNA
   (b) DNA
   (c) RNA
7. (a) phosphate groups
   (b) nitrogenous base
   (c) sugar (ribose or deoxyribose)
8. (a) uracil (U), thymine (T), cytosine (C)
   (b) adenine (A), guanine (G)

1.7, pp. 17–19
6. (c) no
7. competitive inhibitor

Chapter 1 Questions, pp. 21–22
1. d
2. b
3. (a) F
   (b) T
   (c) F
9. reversible inhibition
11. dehydration reaction

2.1, pp. 23–24
3. no
5. tubulin, actin, myosin
6. Microtubules, chromosomes, Microfilaments, microtubules, cilia, flagella, microfilaments, pseudopods

2.2, pp. 25–27
3. (a) integral proteins
   (b) carbohydrate groups
   (c) peripheral protein
   (d) microfilament of cytoskeleton
   (e) integral protein (transport protein)
   (f) cholesterol
5. lipids containing mostly saturated fatty acids
6. reduce, spaces, lipids, gel, reduce, increase
9. transport, triggering signals

2.4, pp. 29–30
2. reactants, waste, CO_2 or H_2O, sugars or ATP
3. (a) hydrophobic molecules, small uncharged molecules
   (b) large polar molecules, ions
5. (a) iii
   (b) ii
   (c) i
6. Step 1: phosphate
   Step 2: binding site, ion
   Step 3: ion
   Step 4: opposite, reduces
   Step 5: released

Chapter 2 Questions, pp. 32–33
1. b
2. d
3. (a) F
   (b) T
5. peripheral membrane protein

Unit 1 Questions, pp. 34–35
1. a
2. c
3. (a) T
   (b) F

Unit 2

3.1, pp. 37–40
6. (a) 16 kJ
   (b) exothermic
7. no
11. catabolic, complex, simpler, released, anabolic, simple, combined, complex, consumed

3.2, pp. 41–42
1. (a) 3 phosphate groups
   (b) ribose
   (c) adenine
3. $ATP + H_2O \rightarrow ADP + P_i$
4. energy, hydrolysis, start, energy, reaction coupling
7. (a) $ATP + H_2O \rightarrow ADP + P_i + energy$; relaxed muscle + energy → contracted muscle
8. (a) −16.3 kJ/mol
   (b) first: endergonic; second: exergonic
   (c) glucose + ATP → glucose-6-phosphate + ADP
   (d) spontaneous

3.3, pp. 43–44
3. (a) F
   (b) F
   (c) T

3.4, pp. 45–46
2. carbon, hydrogen, electrons, high, oxygen, oxidation, carbon–hydrogen, oxygen–hydrogen, energy
4. (a) glucose
   (b) iron
5. (a) (i) carbon becomes oxidized
       (ii) oxygen becomes reduced
7. controlled oxidation
9. (a) reduction of NAD^+
   (b) oxidation of NADH
10. no

Chapter 3 Questions, pp. 48–49
1. d
2. a
3. d
4. b
5. (a) T
   (b) F
   (c) T
7. absorption, release, products, breaking, less, released, forming, endothermic

4.1, pp. 50–51
1. light energy from the sun
2. to produce energy in the form of ATP
3. oxygen, ATP, carbon dioxide, water

4. oxygen, ATP, lactic acid or alcohol
5. (a) outer membrane
   (b) intermembrane space
   (c) matrix
   (d) inner membrane
6. glucose, 2 ATP, 2 pyruvate, 4 ATP, 2 NADH, the cytosol of the cell
7. acetyl-CoA, NAD^+, FAD, CO_2, NADH, $FADH_2$, ATP, the matrix of the mitochondria
8. NADH, $FADH_2$, O_2, ATP, NAD^+, FAD, water, along the inner membrane of the mitochondrion
9. substrate level phosphorylation
10. oxidative phosphorylation
12. (a) obligate, oxygen, aerobic
    (b) energy, oxygen, facultative; Yeast
    (c) energy, obligate, low-oxygen, fermentation, electron transport, anaerobic, inorganic

4.2, pp. 52–54
3. 4 ATP molecules
4. glyceraldehyde-3-phosphate (G3P), dihydroxyacetone phosphate (DHAP)
6. thermal energy (heat), 2 pyruvate, 2 NADH
7. (a) NAD^+
   (b) CoA
   (c) $NADH + H^+$
   (d) CO_2
   (e) acetyl-CoA
9. (a) isocitrate
   (b) α-ketoglutarate
   (c) succinyl CoA
   (d) succinate
   (e) fumarate
   (f) malate
   (g) oxaloacetate
10. (i) aconitase
    (ii) isocitrate dehydrogenase
    (iii) α-ketoglutarate dehydrogenase
    (iv) succinyl CoA synthetase
    (v) succinate dehydrogenase
    (vi) fumarase
    (vii) malate dehydrogenase
    (viii) citrate synthase
12. protons, electrons, complex I, protons
13. protons, electrons, complex II, ubiquinone, protons
14. complex IV
15. forms water (a waste product)
18. oxidative phosphorylation

4.4, pp. 57–58

1. limited or no oxygen, abundant glucose
3. e.g., yeast, some bacteria, humans
6. (a) NADH
   (b) pyruvate
   (c) lactate
   (d) NAD$^+$
8. e.g., sulfur compounds, nitrogen compounds, iron ions

Chapter 4 Summary, p. 61

(a) 2 ATP
(b) 4 H$_2$O
(c) 10 NADH, 2 FADH$_2$
(d) 4 ATP, 2 NADH, 2 H$_2$O
(e) 2 CO$_2$, 2 NADH
(f) 4 CO$_2$, 2 FADH$_2$, 2 ATP, 6 NADH
(g) 4 H$_2$O, 32 ATP

Chapter 4 Questions, pp. 62–63

1. b
2. a
3. (a) F
   (b) F
   (c) T

5.1, pp. 64–66

1. (b) yes
2. ATP, NADPH, oxygen
5. (a) outer membrane
   (b) intermembrane space
   (c) inner membrane
   (d) thylakoid
   (e) thylakoid membrane
   (f) thylakoid lumen
   (g) stroma
   (h) granum
7. (a) CO$_2$
   (b) ADP, P$_i$, NADP$^+$
   (c) ATP, NADPH
   (d) sugars
9. (a) reaction centre with chlorophyll *a*
   (b) transfer of energy
   (c) electron transfer
   (d) primary electron acceptor
   (e) antenna chlorophyll molecules
   (f) carotenoids and other accessory pigments
11. e.g., carotenoids
12. (b) not well

5.2, pp. 67–69

1. (a) water-splitting complex
   (b) P680
   (c) primary electron acceptors
   (d) light
   (e) PQ
   (f) plastocyanin
2. (d) light
   (f) plastocyanin
   (g) P700
   (h) ferredoxin
   (i) NADP$^+$ reductase
   (j) NADP
   (k) NADPH

4. (f) plastocyanin
   (g) P700
   (i) NADP$^+$ reductase
   (j) NADP
   (k) NADPH
   (l) ADP and P$_i$
   (m) ATP
   (n) ATP synthase
6. ADP, NADP$^+$
8. the splitting of water
9. (a) lumen
   (b) to synthesize ATP

5.3, p. 70

2. (a) radioactive, 2 extra neutrons
3. algae *Chorella*

5.4, pp. 71–72

4. (a) CO$_2$
   (b) PEP carboxylase
   (c) oxaloacetate
   (d) malate
   (e) pyruvate
   (f) P$_i$
   (g) AMP + PP$_i$
   (h) PEP
   (i) CO$_2$
   (j) rubisco
   (k) sugar

5.5, p. 73

2. free energized electrons, hydrogen, electricity, hydrogen

5.6, pp. 74–75

3. no

Chapter 5 Questions, pp. 77–78

1. a
2. d
3. (a) T
   (b) F
   (c) T
   (d) F
4. A, C, F
5. the manufacture of ATP
6. ATP, light
7. C, D
8. carbon dioxide, water

Unit 2 Questions, pp. 79–80

1. (a) considerably less
   (b) lower
   (c) matrix of the mitochondrion
   (d) chemical potential, ADP, FAD, NAD$^+$, ATP, FADH$_2$, NADH
   (e) hydrogen, water vapour
2. (a) anaerobic
   (b) anaerobic
   (c) both
   (d) anaerobic
   (e) both
3. (a) both
   (b) both
   (c) anaerobic
   (d) both
   (e) both

(f) aerobic
   (g) aerobic
   (h) anaerobic
   (i) aerobic
7. (a) light, ADP, NADP$^+$, ATP, NADPH
   (b) reduces photorespiration
   (c) limits
   (d) water, glucose
   (e) thylakoid, intermembrane space
10. (a) RuBP, ATP
    (b) no

Unit 3

6.1, pp. 82–83

2. (a) nucleus, mitochondrion, chloroplast
   (b) nucleus
   (c) genome
4. chromosomes, eukaryotes, X, mitosis, meiosis, chromosomes, nucleus
5. no
7. protection, reduced volume
8. 2 sets of chromosomes
10. 46
11. eukaryotes, chromosomes, nucleus, Prokaryotes, loop, nucleoid, loops, plasmids
12. (a) found in loops
    (b) associated with histone-like proteins

6.2, pp. 84–86

5. (a) adenine (A) and thymine (T), guanine (G) and cytosine (C)
   (b) A and T: 2 bonds; G and C: 3 bonds

6.6, pp. 92–93

6. (a) daily exercise, balanced diet
   (b) obesity, sedentary habits, smoking

Chapter 6 Summary, p. 94

1. helicase
2. replication fork
3. single-stranded binding proteins
4. RNA primase
5. RNA primer
6. DNA polymerase III
7. leadings strand
8. lagging strand
9. Okazaki fragment
10. DNA polymerase I
11. DNA ligase

Chapter 6 Questions, pp. 95–96

1. b
2. d
3. c
4. (a) F
   (b) F
   (c) F

11. (a) chromosome in metaphase
    (b) solenoid
    (c) nucleosome
    (d) histones
    (e) DNA double helix

7.1, pp. 97–98

1. c
2. a
5. (a) Francis Crick
9. (a) 64
   (b) 16
   (c) 256
11. Met-Phe-Ala

7.2, pp. 99–100

4. a

7.3, pp. 101–102

3. (a) CAA
   (b) CGG
   (c) UUU
   (d) GGA
5. large, small, mRNA, tRNA, amino acid, mRNA, amino acid, amino acid, tRNA, tRNA, amino acids
7. (a) A site
   (b) P site
   (c) E site

7.4, pp. 103–104

2. b
3. d
4. c
5. (a) *lacI*
   (b) mRNA
   (c) lactose
   (d) inactive repressor
   (e) promoter, operator
   (f) lactose metabolism enzymes

7.5, pp. 105–106

4. errors in DNA replication
5. e.g., radiation, cigarette smoke, car exhaust

7.6, pp. 107–108

1. (a) pseudogene
   (b) LINE
   (c) gene
   (d) SINE
   (e) transposon
   (f) telomere
4. no
5. (c) no

7.7, pp. 109–110

1. ability to reproduce
2. do not produce energy or gather food
4. its RNA genome, reverse transcriptase, integrase, resources, reverse transcriptase, DNA, RNA, integrase, genome, RNA, viruses
6. (a) (i) capsid
       (ii) envelope
   (b) yes

Chapter 7 Questions, pp. 112–113
1. d
2. b
3. a
4. (a) F
   (b) T
   (c) F
   (d) F
5. (a) nucleus
   (b) cytosol
7. point mutation

8.1, pp. 114–115
3. (a) XhoI, sticky; SalI, sticky; AluI, blunt
   (b) HIND III, sticky; SmaI, blunt

8.3, pp. 118–119
1. DNA, genes, functions, proteins, proteins, biopharming, genes, organism, transgenic, genetically modified, germline

8.4, pp. 120–121
1. body, changes, offspring, sperm, eggs, offspring

Chapter 8 Questions, pp. 125–126
1. b
2. d
3. a
4. (a) F
   (b) F
   (c) T
   (d) T
   (e) F
   (f) T
5. covalent bonds, hydrogen bonds
6. 4, 3, 2, 1, 6, 5
8. yes

Unit 3 Questions, pp. 127–128
1. a
2. c
3. (a) F
   (b) F
   (c) T
7. (a) Met-Pro-Gly-Ser-Asn-Phe-Glu-stop
   (c) mutation 1: point insertion, frameshift mutation; mutation 2: point T-C substitution, silent mutation
   (d) mutation 1: Met-Gly-Trp-Val-Glu-Phe-Aug-Ile-Gly; mutation 2: Met-Pro-Gly-Ser-Asn-Phe-Glu-stop
   (e) mutation 1

Unit 4
9.1, pp. 130–131
4. a, b, d, e, f
5. deliver energy, transport chemicals, eliminate waste

9.2, pp. 132–133
2. A: stimulus; B: sensor; C: integrator; D: effector; E: response
4. A: increase in thermal energy; B: thermoreceptors in skin; C: thermoreceptors in hypothalamus; D: sweat gland; E: sweat
5. a, b, c, d, e

9.3, pp. 134–135
9. e.g., endothermic homeotherms: field mice, humans; ectothermic poikilotherms: most lizards, most fish

9.4, pp. 136–137
7. no
8. pH, ionic concentrations
9. byproduct of deamination of proteins; toxic

9.5, pp. 138–139
3. A. Bowman's capsule
   B. proximal convoluted tubule
   C. descending segment of loop of Henle
   D. ascending segment of loop of Henle
   E. distal convoluted tubule
   F. collecting tubule

Chapter 9 Questions, pp. 141–142
1. c
2. d
3. a
4. c
5. (a) T
   (b) T
   (c) F
6. deamination of proteins
7. above its critical temperature
8. frog: reduced; beaver: less change

10.1, pp. 143–144
3. A. hydrophobic hormone
   B. steroid hormone receptor
   C. control
   D. gene
   E. gene activation or inhibition
4. A. hydrophilic hormone
   B. signal
   C. cytosol end of receptor
   D. pathway molecule A
   E. pathway molecule B
   F. pathway molecule C
5. A. hypothalamus
   B. TRH
   C. pituitary
   D. TSH
   E. thyroid hormones
6. sensor: pituitary; integrator: hypothalamus; effector: thyroid hormones

10.2 pp. 145–146
1. A. hypothalamus
   B. pineal gland
   C. pituitary glands
   D. parathyroid glands
   E. thyroid gland
   F. adrenal glands
   G. pancreas
   H. ovaries
   I. testes
2. heart, liver, kidneys, intestines

10.3, pp. 147–148
2. (a) increase
   (b) decrease glucagon secretion
   (c) increase insulin secretion
3. (a) decrease
   (b) increase glucagon secretion
   (c) decrease insulin secretion
4. e.g., hypoglycemia: thirst, fatigue, weight loss; hyperglycemia: shaking, hunger, weakness

10.5, pp. 150–151
1. steroid hormone receptor, cytosol, binding site, hormone, hormone, nucleus, steroid hormone response element, gene, hormone, steroid hormone receptor, steroid hormone response element, gene, protein

10.7, pp. 153–155
1. A. oviduct
   B. ovary
   C. uterus
   D. urinary bladder
   E. urethra
   F. clitoris
   G. labia minora
   H. labia majora
   I. vagina
2. A. urinary bladder
   B. seminal vesicle
   C. prostate gland
   D. urethra
   E. erectile tissue
   F. penis
   G. testes
   H. scrotum
   I. epididymis
   J. vas deferens
   K. bulbourethral gland
5. Follicle stimulating, pituitary gland, estrogen, ovary, ovulation, progesterone, oviduct, sperm cell, zygote, oviduct, embryo, uterus, human chorionic gonadotropin (hCG), corpus luteum, estrogen, progesterone, uterine lining, menstruation
7. seminiferous, testes, Sertoli, nutrients, blood, Leydig, epididymis, vas deferens

Chapter 10 Questions, pp. 157–158
1. b
2. c
3. (a) T
   (b) F
   (c) F
   (d) F
   (e) T
4. diabetes insipidus
5. (a) Mr. Yamamoto
   (b) Ms. Desai
6. hyperactive thyroid
7. c
8. receptors, Steroid, Protein
9. prostaglandin
12. e.g., oxytocin
15. corpus luteum
16. insulin

11.1, pp. 159–161
1. (a) cell body
   (b) dendrites
   (c) axons
   (d) axon terminals
2. A. dendrites
   B. cell body
   C. nucleus
   D. axon hillock
   E. axon
   F. axon terminals
4. A. sensory receptor
   B. dendrite of sensory (afferent) neuron
   C. afferent neuron cell body
   D. afferent neuron axon terminal
   E. cell body of interneuron
   F. axon of interneuron
   G. axon terminal of interneuron
   H. axon of motor (efferent) neuron
   I. axon terminal of motor (efferent) neuron at effector
   J. spinal cord
6. A. central nervous system (CNS)
   B. peripheral nervous system (PNS)
   C. input to CNS
   D. output from CNS
   E. afferent system
   F. efferent system
   G. somatic system
   H. sympathetic system
   I. parasympathetic system
   J. skeletal muscles
   K. effectors

11.2, pp. 162–163
4. 4, 2, 1, 5, 3

11.3, pp. 164–166
1. A. white matter
   B. afferent neuron
   C. efferent neuron
   D. interneuron
   E. grey matter
   F. ventral root
   G. dorsal root

2. A. cerebrum
   B. corpus callosum
   C. thalamus
   D. mammillary body
   E. hypothalamus
   F. pituitary gland
   G. brain stem
   H. pons
   I. medulla oblongata
   J. spinal cord
   K. cerebellum
   L. midbrain
5. hemisphere, right cerebral hemisphere, sensory, movements, left, nonverbal, art and music, spatial, left cerebral hemisphere, sensory, movements, right, language, abstract, mathematics, Axon, corpus callosum
9. hypothalamus

11.4, pp. 167–168
2. spinal, peripheral, spinal, motor neurons, ventral, skeletal, dendrites, cell bodies, in, axons, skeletal muscle
5. both

11.5, pp. 169–171
1. (a) mechanoreceptors
   (b) photoreceptors
   (c) chemoreceptors
   (d) mechanoreceptors
   (e) thermoreceptors
   (f) nociceptors
   (g) chemoreceptors
2. A. lens
   B. cornea
   C. pupil
   D. iris
   E. retina
   F. blind spot
   G. optic nerve
3. A. auditory canal; 1
   B. eardrum; 2
   C. malleus; 3
   D. incus; 3
   E. stapes; 3
   F. oval window; 4
   G. cochlea; 5
   H. auditory nerve; 6
   J. semicircular canals
5. (a) detect changes in temperature
   (b) skin, hypothalamus

Chapter 11 Questions, pp. 175–176
1. d
2. a
3. b
4. a
5. (a) T
   (b) F
   (c) T
8. pons, medulla oblongata
11. dendrite
12. central nervous system

Unit 4 Questions, pp. 177–178
1. c
2. d
3. d
4. (a) F
   (b) T
   (c) T
   (d) F
5. glucocorticoids
6. (a) during ovulation
   (b) hypothalamus begins secreting GnRH
   (c) lack of estrogen and progesterone
   (d) estrogen
7. (a) Mr. Morgan
   (b) Ms. Wong
   (c) Mr. Capelli

Unit 5

12.1, pp. 180–182
2. (a) population density
3. e.g., elk, beluga whales
4. (a) clumped dispersion
   (b) uniform dispersion
   (c) random dispersion
5. dispersion, food, uniform, clumped, food, shelter
6. tracks, nests, fecal droppings

12.2, pp. 183–184
1. population change = (births + immigration) – (deaths + emigration)
3. plentiful, climate, increase, scarce, precipitation, decrease
5. a, b, e
7. 0.62 or 62%

12.3, pp. 185–187
2. population decreasing by small amount

3. (a) 0.12 births per individual per year
   (b) 0.09 deaths per individual per year
5. 2^6 or 64 cells
7. (a) exponential growth
8. 7.67 years
9. (a) geometric growth
12. K, plenty, 1, maximum, K, few, small, low
13. (b) no

12.4, pp. 188–189
3. density, increase
5. no
6. asexual reproduction
7. density, stay the same
8. (a) e.g., sudden hot or cold spells, fires, earthquakes, storms
   (b) climate change

12.5, pp. 190–192
1. (a) mutualism
   (b) competition
   (c) commensalism
   (d) predation, herbivory, parasitism
2. (a) mutualism
   (b) parasitism
   (c) commensalism
   (d) parasitism
   (e) mutualism
7. (a) darker line
11. (a) increase
   (b) decrease
   (c) decrease
   (d) decrease
12. reduced ecosystem diversity

Chapter 12 Questions, pp. 194–195
1. c
2. b
3. (a) F
   (b) F
8. a forest fire
9. sunlight, soil moisture, inorganic nutrients, food type, food size, nesting sites, niches

13.1, pp. 196–198
7. Inuit
9. birth, death, high, rises, improves, rapidly, drop, slow, death rate, decreases

13.2, pp. 199–201
2. transportation, energy, pollution, landfills, inefficient, goods and services, resources
3. (a) e.g., India, much of Africa
   (b) e.g., North America, Australia
8. primary consumers: 50 kJ; secondary consumers: 5 kJ
10. (a) e.g., farming, logging, construction
12. e.g., alternate crops, add fertilizer
1 5. e.g., burning fossil fuels, emissions from manufacturing

13.4, pp. 203–204
2. (a) e.g., soil degradation, desertification, deforestation
   (b) e.g., sustainable agriculture, forest regeneration
4. e.g., universal education, gender equality, environmental sustainability
5. (a) Ontario

13.5, p. 205
1. Living Planet Index, Global Footprint
2. (a) seventh largest per capita of all countries studied

Chapter 13 Questions, pp. 207–208
1. b
2. a
3. (a) F
   (b) T
4. science, technology, medicine, limits, erosion, habitat, drainage, extinctions
6. erosion, lost fertility, desertification, increased salinization
9. industrial, greener, gasoline, electricity

Unit 5 Questions, pp. 209–210
1. d
2. d
3. (a) F
   (b) F
7. wheat, rice, corn

Appendix

A-1 Taking Notes: Identifying the Main Ideas

- *Identify and highlight the main ideas.* Main ideas are key concepts within a text. Text features such as headings, subheadings, boldfaced or italicized words, and graphic clues help to identify the main ideas in a text.
- *Identify and underline the details.* Details clarify or elaborate on the main ideas within a text.
- When you study for an exam, focus on the main ideas, not the details.

EXAMPLE

Polysaccharides

A **polysaccharide molecule** is a chain of monosaccharides with many subunits joined by glycosidic linkages. A polysaccharide is a macromolecule, which is a very large molecule assembled by the covalent linkage of smaller subunit molecules. The dehydration synthesis reactions that assemble polysaccharides are examples of polymerization. **Polymerization** is the process in which identical or variable subunits, called **monomers**, link together in a long chain to form a larger molecule. This molecule is called a **polymer**, hence the term "polymerization." The linkage of non-identical subunits creates highly diverse and varied biological molecules. Many kinds of polymers are found in cells, not just polysaccharides. For example DNA is another type of a polymer.

The most common polysaccharides are plant starches, glycogen, and cellulose. They are assembled from hundreds or thousands of glucose units. Cellulose is the main component of plant cell walls and the most abundant organic molecule on Earth. Cellulose molecules are long and straight and have very large numbers of polar OH groups. These two features enable many cellulose molecules to assemble side by side and form hundreds and thousands of hydrogen bonds. These numerous hydrogen bonds give cellulose fibres their great strength. Other polysaccharides form from a variety of different sugar monomers. Polysaccharides may be linear unbranched molecules, or they may contain branches in which side chains of sugar units attach to a main chain.

Description/Discussion of Strategies

Read the sample text above and note the text features. Remember that text features such as headings and boldfaced words signal key concepts. Notice that the above text has the heading "Polysaccharides." The heading is a text feature that tells you the topic of the text. It gives you important information and is, therefore, a main idea. Highlight the heading. Now look at the boldfaced words in the text: **polysaccharide molecule**, **polymerization**, **monomer**, and **polymer**. Boldfaced words identify vocabulary terms. Here, the boldfaced words are embedded in vocabulary definitions and tell you what the words mean. Highlight vocabulary definitions as they are main ideas, too. Finally, take a look at the opening sentences in both paragraphs of the above text. The opening sentences give you a quick overview of the information in the two paragraphs and should also be highlighted as main ideas.

Now that you have identified the main ideas in the above text, try to find the details. Look for sentences that add to the main ideas you identified above. The sentence "Cellulose is the main component of plant cell walls and the most abundant molecule on Earth" is an illustration of the sentence "The most common polysaccharides are plant starches, glycogen, and cellulose." It is a detail, and should be underlined. Similarly, the last two sentences of the first paragraph are also details because they tell more about polysaccharides, the main idea. Underline the two sentences.

PRACTICE

Read the following text and complete the activities below.

Phospholipids

Cells could not exist without the phosphate-containing lipids, called phospholipids. Phospholipids are the primary lipids of cell membranes. In the most common phospholipids, as in triglycerides, glycerol forms the backbone of the molecules. Only two of its binding sites, however, link to fatty acids. The third site links to a charged phosphate group, which often binds to another polar or charged unit. Thus a phospholipid contains two hydrophobic fatty acids at one end, attached to a hydrophilic polar group, often called the head group. Molecules that contain both hydrophobic and hydrophilic regions are called amphipathic molecules. The head of an amphipathic molecule is the polar and hydrophilic region. The tail is the hydrophobic lipid, which is composed of a carbon chain.

1. Highlight the main ideas in the text.
2. Underline the details in the text.

Now read the following text and answer the questions that follow.

Waxes

Waxes are large lipid molecules that are made of long fatty acid chains linked to alcohols or carbon rings. Waxes are hydrophobic, extremely non-polar, and soft solids over a wide range of temperatures. These characteristics are what makes them ideal for flexible waterproof coatings on various plant and animal parts. One type of wax, cutin, is produced by certain plant cells to form a water-resistant coating on the surfaces of stems, leaves, and fruit. Cutin enables plants to conserve water, and it acts as a barrier to infections and diseases. Such functions are vital for life. Without this waxy coating, plants could not survive on land. Birds secrete a waxy material that helps to keep their feathers dry. Bees produce beeswax to make their honeycombs.

1. Which sentence from the text contains a main idea?
   (a) Birds secrete a waxy material that helps to keep their feathers dry.
   (b) Bees produce beeswax to make their honeycombs.
   (c) Waxes are hydrophobic, extremely non-polar, and soft solids over a wide range of temperatures.
   (d) Cutin enables plants to conserve water, and it acts as a barrier to infections and diseases.
2. Explain the difference between a main idea and a detail.

A-1 Taking Notes: Reading Strategies

The skills and strategies that you use to help you read depend on the type of material you are reading. Reading a science book is different from reading a novel. When you are reading a science book, you are reading for information.

BEFORE READING

Skim the section you are going to read. Look at the illustrations, headings, and subheadings.

- *Preview.* What is this section about? How is it organized?
- *Make connections.* What do I already know about the topic? How is it connected to other topics I already know about?
- *Predict.* What information will I find in this section? Which parts provide the most information?
- *Set a purpose.* What questions do I have about the topic?

DURING READING

Pause and think as you read. Spend time on the photographs, illustrations, tables, and graphs, as well as on the words.

- *Check your understanding.* What are the main ideas in this section? How would I state them in my own words? What questions do I still have? Should I reread? Do I need to read more slowly, or can I read more quickly?
- *Determine the meanings of key science terms.* Can I figure out the meanings of terms from context clues in the words or illustrations? Do I understand the definitions in bold type? Is there something about the structure of a new term that will help me remember its meaning? Which terms should I look up in the glossary?
- *Make inferences.* What conclusions can I make from what I am reading? Can I make any conclusions by "reading between the lines"?
- *Visualize.* What mental pictures can I make to help me understand and remember what I am reading? Should I make a sketch?
- *Make connections.* How is the information in this section like information I already know?
- *Interpret visuals and graphics.* What additional information can I get from the photographs, illustrations, tables, or graphs?

AFTER READING

Many of the strategies you use during reading can also be used after reading. For example, your textbook provides summaries and questions at the ends of sections. These questions will help you check your understanding and make connections to information you have just read or to other parts in the textbook.

At the end of each chapter are summary questions and a vocabulary list, followed by a Chapter Self-Quiz and Chapter Review.

- *Locate needed information.* Where can I find the information I need to answer the questions? Under what heading might I find the information? What terms in bold type should I look for? What details do I need to include in my answers?
- *Synthesize.* How can I organize the information? What graphic organizer could I use? What headings or categories could I use?
- *React.* What are my opinions about this information? How does it, or might it, affect my life or my community? Do other students agree with my reactions? Why or why not?
- *Evaluate information.* What do I know now that I did not know before? Have any of my ideas changed because of what I have read? What questions do I still have?

A-1 Taking Notes: Graphic Organizers

Graphic organizers are diagrams that are used to organize and display ideas visually. Graphic organizers are especially useful in science and technology studies when you are trying to connect together different concepts, ideas, and data. Different organizers have different purposes. They can be used to

- show processes
- organize ideas and thinking
- compare and contrast
- show properties of characteristics
- review words and terms
- collaborate and share ideas

TO SHOW PROCESSES

Graphic organizers can show the stages in a process (**Figure 1**).

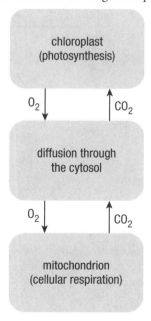

Figure 1 This graphic organizer shows that oxygen and carbon dioxide are transported throughout the plant cell.

TO ORGANIZE IDEAS AND THINKING

A **concept map** is a diagram showing the relationships between ideas (**Figure 2**). Words or pictures representing ideas are connected by arrows and words or expressions that explain the connections. You can use a concept map to brainstorm what you already know, to map your thinking, or to summarize what you have learned.

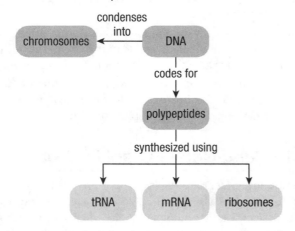

Figure 2 Concept maps show the relationships among ideas.

Mind maps are similar to concept maps, but they do not have explanations for the connections between ideas.

You can use a **tree diagram** to show concepts that can be broken down into smaller categories (**Figure 3**).

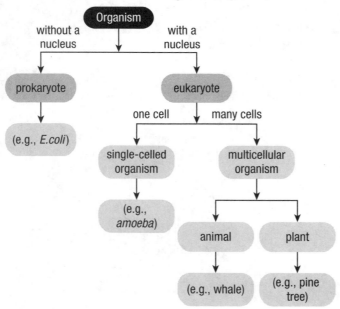

Figure 3 Tree diagrams are very useful for classification.

You can use a **fishbone diagram** to organize the important ideas under the major concepts of a topic that you are studying (**Figure 4**).

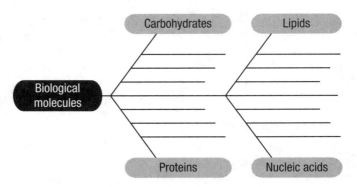

Figure 4 A fishbone diagram.

You can use a **K-W-L** chart to write down what you know (K), what you want (W) to find out, and, afterwards, what you have learned (L) (**Figure 5**).

K	W	L
What I know	What I want to know	What I have learned

Figure 5 A K-W-L chart.

TO COMPARE AND CONTRAST

You can use a **compare-and-contrast chart** to show similarities and differences between two substances, actions, ideas, and so on (**Figure 6**).

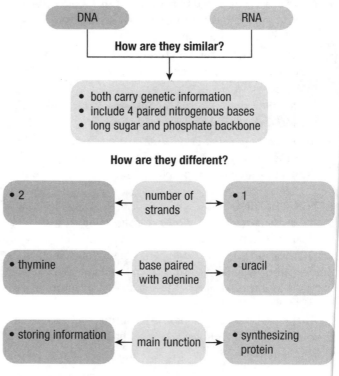

Figure 6 A compare-and-contrast chart.

You can use a **comparison matrix** (a type of table) to compare related concepts (**Table 1**).

Table 1 Subatomic Particles

	Proton	**Neutron**	**Electron**
electrical charge	positive	neutral	negative
symbol	p+	n^0	e$^-$
location	nucleus	nucleus	orbit around the nucleus

You can use a **Venn diagram** to show similarities and differences (**Figure 7**).

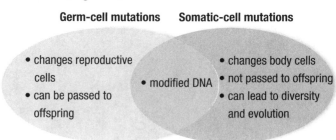

Figure 7 A Venn diagram.

TO SHOW PROPERTIES OR CHARACTERISTICS

You can use a **bubble map** to show properties or characteristics (**Figure 8**).

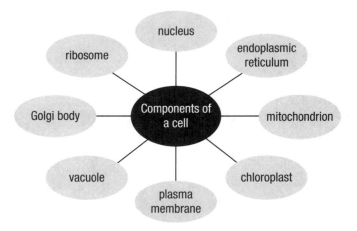

Figure 8 A bubble map.

TO REVIEW WORDS AND TERMS

You use a **word wall** to list, in no particular order, the key words and concepts for a topic (**Figure 9**).

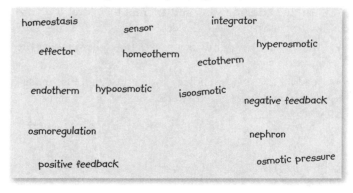

Figure 9 A word wall.

TO COLLABORATE AND SHARE IDEAS

When you are working in a small group, you can use a **placemat organizer** to write down what you know about a certain topic. Then all group members discuss their answers and write in the middle section what you have in common (**Figure 10**).

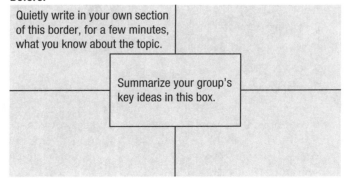

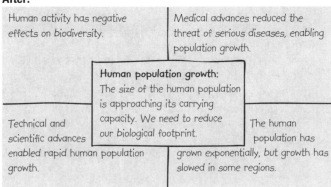

Figure 10 A placemat organizer.

A-2 Answering Questions
A-2.1 Multiple-Choice Questions

- Read the question stem and attempt to answer it before looking at the answer choices.
- Analyze the key words or phrases that tell you what the question stem is asking.
- Read all the answer choices and choose one that most closely matches your answer.
- If your answer is not among the answer choices, reread the question stem. Sometimes slowing your reading pace can help you better understand the meaning of the question.
- Cross out any answer choices that you know are incorrect.

EXAMPLE

Read the following question stem:

In which region of the nephron does reabsorption first occur?

Description/Discussion of Strategies

Try to answer the question first without looking at the answer options. (Cover the options with a sheet of paper or with your hand.) Then, look at the answer options below. Check your answer against the four choices given. Is your answer among the options? If yes, you have correctly answered the question.

(a) Bowman's capsule

(b) proximal convoluted tubule

(c) loop of Henle

(d) efferent arteriole

If your answer does not match one of the options, use the next strategy. Note the key words in the sample question. They key words and phrases are the essence of the question. They tell you what the question is expecting you to know or do. This sample question asks you to recognize a "region" of the nephron that is the first one involved in "reabsorption".

Look at the answer options. Which of them is a "region" of the kidney? Are there any answer options that you know are wrong? You probably know that the efferent arteriole is part of the circulatory system, not of the nephron, so you can eliminate answer choice (d).

You have narrowed your possible answers to (a), (b), and (c). You may know that Bowman's capsule is the first region the unfiltered blood passes through. Since no filtration has taken place yet, it is unlikely reabsorption would occur. You may also know that the blood passes through the proximal convoluted tubule before it passes through the loop of Henle. So choice (b) seems to be the best choice, and it is indeed correct.

PRACTICE

Complete the following multiple-choice questions using the tips you just read.

1. Which of the following is involved in glycolysis?

    (a) the electron transport chain

    (b) co-enzyme A

    (c) pyruvate

    (d) the mitochondrial matrix

    Explain how you arrived at the answer to the above question.

2. Which DNA sequence is complementary with 5' TATGGCAT 3'

    (a) 5' ATACCGTA 3'

    (b) 3' ATACCGTA 5'

    (c) 5' AUACCGUA 3'

    (d) 3' AUACCGUA 5'

    What answer choices were you able to eliminate? Why?

3. Which of the following hormones is not controlled by the pituitary gland?

    (a) testosterone

    (b) estrogen

    (c) thyroxin

    (d) insulin

    Were there any key words in the stem that helped you identify what you were expected to know? Explain.

A-2.2 Short-Answer Questions

A **short-answer question** is an open-ended question that requires a response. The question could ask for a definition, an explanation, or an example. It could also be a calculation or a completion activity. Depending on the type of short-answer question, the response will vary in length from a single sentence to a few sentences.

- Read the question carefully to understand the type of response required.
- Organize your response before writing it by making an outline, listing main points, drawing a sketch, or creating a graphic organizer.
- Make sure you answer all parts of the question. Eliminate any unnecessary information from your answer so it is clear and concise.

SHORT-ANSWER QUESTIONS

Read the following selection and answer the short-answer question:

RNA: Ribonucleic Acid

Like DNA, ribonucleic acid (RNA) is a carrier of genetic information. However, RNA differs from DNA in many ways. First, ribonucleic acid contains a ribose sugar rather than a deoxyribose sugar. A ribose sugar has a hydroxyl group on its 2′ carbon. Second, instead of thymine, RNA contains the base uracil. Uracil is similar in structure to thymine, except thymine has a methyl group on its 1′ carbon. Uracil in the RNA pairs with adenine in the DNA strand. Third, DNA is double stranded, whereas RNA is single stranded. When a gene is transcribed into RNA, only a single-stranded complementary copy is made. In the complementary copy, uracil is substituted for thymine.

1. Compare and contrast DNA and RNA.

Description/Discussion of Strategies

Read the question and identify what type of short-answer question it is. This sample question asks you to compare and contrast two types of molecule. In other words, the question requires an answer that is at least a couple of sentences long. Notice that five lines have been provided for you to write your answer. The sample notes below list the main points regarding DNA and RNA.

SAMPLE STUDENT NOTES:

DNA	RNA
– carries genetic information	– also carries genetic information
– contains deoxyribose sugar	– contains ribose sugar
– contains the base thymine	– contains the base uracil
– contains adenine, cytosine, guanine	– contains adenine, cytosine, guanine
– double stranded	– single stranded

You will build your answer from these bullet points. Highlight the bullet points that are similar and group them together in your answer. Group the differences together in your answer.

Finally, eliminate any information in your answer that is unnecessary or that does not pertain to the question. If your response is very long, condense the information to make it brief and succinct.

Both DNA and RNA contain the bases adenine, guanine, and cytosine and carry genetic information in the cell. DNA also contains the base thymine and a deoxyribose sugar in a double-stranded backbone. RNA contains the base uracil and a ribose sugar on a single-stranded backbone.

PRACTICE

Complete the following short-answer questions using the selections below and the tips you just read.

The Issue: Using Transgenic Plants and Animals

One reason for the expanding research on using genetically modified plants and animals as protein factories is cost. Methods in which animal or plant DNA is modified to produce proteins are usually more economical than operating a laboratory with controlled bacterial populations. As a result, the cheaper insulin from safflowers, for example, could improve the lives of diabetics in the developing world. Another reason for using plants and animals is that larger organisms can produce larger, more complex, molecules. Because genetic engineering is a new biotechnology, however, many people are concerned that there may be risks associated with its use. For example, it is possible that genetically modified canola could outcompete native or non-modified species or become a weed.

1. What is one advantage and one disadvantage of using genetically modified plants and animals to produce proteins?

Types of Hormones

There are more than 60 known hormones and local regulators in humans. They are identified by their chemical structure. There are two main types of hormones. **Protein hormones** consist of amino acid chains, ranging in length from as few as three amino acids to more than 200. They are released into the blood or extracellular fluid by the cells in the endocrine glands where they are produced. Protein hormones are usually hydrophilic and many act on receptors on the cell membrane. One group of hormones, the growth factors, regulates the division and differentiation of many types of cells in the body.

Steroid hormones are derived from cholesterol and are not very soluble in blood. However, they can pass easily through the lipid bilayer of cellular membranes, and act on receptors inside the cell. Some steroid hormones have very similar structures but produce very different results. For example, testosterone and estradiol, two major sex hormones, are responsible for the development of male and female characteristics, respectively, but differ only in the presence or absence of a single methyl group.

2. What is the difference between protein hormones and steroid hormones?

Population Cycles

Predation is an example of an interspecific interaction in which the population density of one species (predator) increases while the population of the other species (prey) decreases. Once the predator population reaches a level where it is difficult to find enough food, it begins to decrease. Fluctuations in the predator population follow fluctuations in the prey population through time, with the prey population increasing while the predator population is still decreasing and the prey population decreasing while the predator population is still increasing. The predator-prey relationship can have a significant impact on the size of both populations.

3. Describe the characteristics of a predator–prey population cycle.

A2.3 True/False Questions

Many true or false questions connect two ideas, or a person with an idea.
- Read the statement carefully.
- Identify the main ideas in the statement.
- Decide whether the ideas are connected or not.

EXAMPLE

Decide whether the following statement is true or false.

The central dogma states that each type of protein is translated by a specific RNA sequence.

Description/Discussion of Strategies

Read the question carefully. This question consists of three concepts: the central dogma, protein translation, and a specific RNA sequence. Underline each concept in the statement.

Decide which concepts are connected.
- Does the central dogma relate to protein translation?
- Does the central dogma relate to RNA sequences?
- Does an RNA sequence determine which protein is formed?

If all three answers are yes, the statement is true. If either is false, the statement is false. This statement is FALSE, DNA sequences determine the type of protein.

PRACTICE

Classify the statement as either true or false using the tips you have just read.

1. A change in the strength of a nerve impulse determines the strength of a muscle contraction.

What two concepts did you identify in the statement?

A-2.4 Matching Questions

Matching questions typically present two lists. The task is to match items from the first list with items from the second list.

- Study the items on the first list, and ensure that you understand the common characteristic of all of the items.

- Study the items on the first list, and ensure that you understand the common characteristic of all of the items.
- Look for obvious matches that you can recognize immediately.
- Then, continue with less obvious matches.
- Even if there are some items that you are not familiar with or cannot remember, you can often reduce the choices available.

EXAMPLE

Match the hormone on the left with an associated endocrine gland on right.

(a) insulin　　　　　　　(i) pituitary gland

(b) FSH　　　　　　　　(ii) pancreas alpha cells

(c) estrogen　　　　　　(iii) pancreas beta cells

(d) adrenalin　　　　　 (iv) adrenal gland

(e) glucagon　　　　　　(v) ovary

Description/Discussion of Strategies

Start by checking the common characteristics: all items on the first list are hormones, and all items on the second list are endocrine glands.

Next, look for any obvious matches. Most people associate estrogen with the ovary and adrenalin with the adrenal gland. Continue making matches. If there are two or more left that you do not know, you may need to make an educated guess. For example, the two areas of the pancreas may present a difficult choice.

PRACTICE

Match the compound on the left with the metabolic process on the right.

(a) pyruvate　　　　　　(i) anaerobic cellular respiration

(b) fumerate　　　　　　(ii) glycolysis

(c) ferredoxin　　　　　 (iii) citric acid cycle

(d) NADH　　　　　　　(iv) photosynthesis

(e) ethanol　　　　　　 (v) aerobic cellular respiration

Which matches did you find easiest to make? Which matches did you have to guess at?

A-2.5 Extended Response Questions

Extended-response questions take more thought and planning than shorter responses do. The quality of your response will determine the mark you will receive. You must prepare by being very familiar with all aspects of the topic that the question is based on.

Most extended responses include:

- An introductory paragraph that introduces your main idea or the point you intend to make in your answer. You can often restate the question as all or part of your introduction.

- A core section that provides information, examples, and possibly simple sketches to support and flesh out the main idea. Include all that you know about the topic that is relevant to the question being asked. In most cases, one paragraph will be enough for this section, but you may need more paragraphs if there is more than one main idea in the question or in your response.

- A final concluding paragraph that sums up your main idea. You can include a restatement of your main idea similar to the first paragraph. Phrase your sentences in the concluding paragraph as definite, confident statements.

EXAMPLE

1. Genetic engineering can now transfer genes from one organism to another with predictable results. Provide arguments for and against the use of this technology.

Description/Discussion of Strategies

Decide on your main ideas. The number of marks allotted to a question is often a good clue about how many main ideas to include. Jot down as many ideas as come to mind. You need not use all of them, but you can select the most important or relevant ones from your list.

Describe possible applications of genetic engineering and their potential for good or harm.

SAMPLE STUDENT IDEAS:

Arguments for: Agricultural production can be increased by plants that need less fertilizer or pesticides, have higher nutrient content, longer storage times. Human medicines, such as insulin, can be commercially produced by bacteria. Viral vectors may be able to insert functioning genes directly into human tissues.

Arguments against: Transgenic organisms may outcompete and replace native species. Increased monoculture may harm biodiversity in food crops. Bacteria or viral vectors may escape into environment as new diseases. Introduced proteins may trigger food allergies. Inserted genes may trigger cancers.

Now, use your ideas to write an introductory paragraph.

SAMPLE INTRODUCTORY PARAGRAPH

Genetic engineering has increased agricultural production and been used to develop medicines. However, it may prove to cause environmental and health problems.

Next, use your ideas to give examples of your main points. It is not necessary to use all of the ideas. Use the number of marks allotted and the space allowed for the answer to guide the length of your response. For just a few marks, or in a small space, include at least one example of the technology's potential for good, and at least one example of its potential for harm.